INTERNATIONAL SERIES OF MONOGRAPHS IN
ANALYTICAL CHEMISTRY

GENERAL EDITORS: R. BELCHER AND H. FREISER

VOLUME 46

CHEMICAL ANALYSIS OF ADDITIVES IN PLASTICS

CHEMICAL ANALYSIS
OF
ADDITIVES IN PLASTICS

BY

T. R. CROMPTON

B.Sc., M.Sc., F.R.I.C.

PERGAMON PRESS

Oxford · New York · Toronto

Sydney · Braunschweig

Pergamon Press Ltd., Headington Hill Hall, Oxford
Pergamon Press Inc., Maxwell House, Fairview Park, Elmsford, New York 10523
Pergamon of Canada Ltd., 207 Queen's Quay West, Toronto 1
Pergamon Press (Aust.) Pty. Ltd., 19a Boundary Street, Rushcutters Bay,
N.S.W. 2011, Australia
Vieweg & Sohn GmbH, Burgplatz 1, Braunschweig

First edition 1971

Library of Congress Catalog Card No. 71–161452

Printed in Great Britain by A. Wheaton & Co. Exeter

08 016627 X

This book is dedicated to my wife
Elisabeth

CONTENTS

PREFACE

THIS book is designed as a practical text for use in the laboratories of the plastics manufacturing and plastics user industries and for use by others such as research institutions and universities who are interested in problems associated with additives and adventitious impurities present in polymers.

Whilst several very excellent books already exist on the analysis of plastics and rubbers, it was evident to the author that little attempt had been made to gather together and publish the scattered and voluminous literature now existing on the subject of the characterization, identification and determination of various types of additives in plastics. It is sincerely hoped that this book will help remedy the situation.

Ashton-on-Mersey
June 1970

T. R. CROMPTON

ACKNOWLEDGEMENTS

THE illustrations in this book are from a variety of sources. Reproduction of the following illustrations and tables is authorized through the courtesy of the publications named herewith.

Analytical Chemistry, American Chemical Society, 1155 Sixteenth Street, N.W. Washington 6DC. Figures 7, 8, 27, 45, 46, 47 and 48. Tables 2, 14, 15, 16, 17, 18, 19, 20 and 42.

The Society for Analytical Chemistry, 9/10 Savile Row, London W1X 1AF. Figures 19, 20, 25, 26, 55, 56, 57, 58, 60 and 61. Table 25.

Pergamon Press Ltd., Headington Hill Hall, Oxford, OX3 0BW. Figures 33, 50, 51, 52, 53, 69, 70 and 71. Tables 1, 7, 32, 38 and 43.

Springer-Verlag-Wein/New York, Mol kerbastei 5, A-1010 Vienna, Austria. Figures 28 and 29.

Laboratory Practice, 9 Gough Square, Fleet Street, London E.C.4. Figures 23, 24, 38, 39, 40, 41 and 43. Table 36.

I.P.C. Business Press Ltd., 33–40 Bowling Green Lane, London E.C.1. Figures 10, 11, 12, 13, 14, 15, 16 and 17. Tables 8, 9, 10, 11, 12, 21, 23 and 31.

Materie Plastiche ed Elastomerie, Revista Mensile Fondata Nel 1935 Editrice, l'Industria srl 20129 Milano via Farneti 8, Italy. Figures 34 and 35.

Elsevier Publishing Co., Jan Van Galenstraat 335, P.O. Box 211, Amsterdam, Netherlands. Figures 30, 31 and 32. Table 26.

Rubber Age, 101 West 31st Street, New York 10001, New York, U.S.A. Figure 9.

Association of Official Analytical Chemists, Box 540 Benjamin Franklin Station, Washington DC 20044, Washington, U.S.A. Figure 22.

The Institution of the Rubber Industry, 4 Kensington Palace Gardens, London W.8. Figure 36. Tables 27, 28, 29 and 30.

The Institute of Petroleum, 61 New Cavendish Street, London W1M 8AR. Figure 37. Table 35.

The Plastics Institute, 11 Hobart Place, London, S.W.1. Figures 62, 63, 64, 65, 66, 67 and 68. Tables 39 and 44.

The author also wishes to acknowledge assistance from Mr. R. Powers for his help in obtaining addresses of authors and publishers, Mrs. Christine Squirrel for typing part of the manuscript, and his wife, Elisabeth, for typing, proof reading and her encouragement throughout.

CHAPTER 1

QUANTITATIVE DETERMINATION
OF KNOWN ADDITIVES

1.1 General Discussion

In order to appreciate fully the techniques which have been developed for the analysis of additives in polymers, it is necessary to be familiar with the difficulties involved in such an undertaking and also with the chemical and physical properties of the additives themselves.

Most of the analytical problems arise from three factors: the situation of the additive in a more or less insoluble polymer matrix, the high reactivity and low stability of many types of additives, especially antioxidants, and the low concentrations of additives present in many instances in the polymer matrix. The first factor severely limits the choice of analytical techniques that can be applied to the sample without prior separation of the additive from the polymer, a procedure which is itself hindered by the nature of the polymer matrix. In addition, any extract of the polymer is liable to contamination by low molecular weight polymer "wax" which may interfere with subsequent analysis and is difficult to remove.

The second and third factors mentioned above combine to make the handling of extracts an exacting job if quantitative information is required. Antioxidants, particularly, are labile unstable compounds, forming complex decomposition products; this considerably complicates interpretation of analytical data, and any loss of material by decomposition is liable to be significant since the quantities present are initially so low. The writer[16] and others, for example, have recommended that polymer extracts are kept in actinic glassware and used for subsequent analysis without delay. If any storage of solutions is necessary, this should be done under nitrogen, in the dark and in a refrigerator to minimize the effects of oxygen, light and heat on any labile compounds present. Lorenz et al.[17] have published data on sample changes during handling of antioxidant extracts, including losses during concentration by evaporation. Generally, however, this aspect of additive analysis does not seem to have received the consideration it deserves.

Apart from these factors which complicate the processing of the sample, there are others which complicate the interpretation of the data obtained, the principal ones being the wide range of additives used nowadays in polymer technology, which makes positive identification difficult by all but the most sophisticated analytical techniques; the presence of several types of additives in a single polymer formulation, e.g. plasticizers, ultraviolet stabilizers, slip agents and possibly two antioxidants, one for processing and one for service, may all be present in a single formulation; and finally, depending on processing history and age of the polymer, the possibility that additive decomposition products may also be present to

1

complicate the analytical problem in hand. The latter type of additive decomposition should be distinguished from that occurring during analytical processing. For example, a particular type of polymer additive may undergo partial thermal degradation during extrusion operations involved in its manufacture and then during analysis may degrade by another route under the influence of light.

To summarize then, the determination of additives in polymers presents the analyst with some difficult problems. Only small concentrations are present, complex mixtures may be involved and, moreover, frequently the mixture is of compounds of completely unknown type.

1.2   Direct Spectroscopy of Polymer Films

The difficulties involved in the extraction of additives from polymers have lead to a search for analytical techniques not involving a prior solvent separation of an additive extract. Of all the techniques tried, only those based on spectroscopy can claim any measure of success. Luongo[18] has tried ultraviolet examination of thin, hot-pressed polymer films. Using a double-beam spectrophotometer with air in the reference beam, he was able to estimate antioxidant levels ranging from 0·002 to 1·0% in polyethylene. Such a procedure is limited in that the polymer must exhibit a relatively flat absorption curve in the wavelength range used; also many antioxidants exhibit similar or identical spectra.

Miller and Willis[19] obtained infrared spectra of antioxidants from polymer films in a similar way, except that they compensated with additive-free polymer in the reference beam. Infrared spectroscopy is more specific than ultraviolet spectroscopy, but some workers[20] find that the antioxidant level in polymers is too low to give suitable spectra. Drushel and Sommers[21] combined specificity with simplicity by using spectrofluorimetric and phosphorescence techniques. Again, they used a double-beam spectrophotometer, this time with a wedge of additive-free polymer in the reference beam. They admit that the method is only applicable if the antioxidant has distinct sharp bands, and if no other components exhibit intense absorption in the same region.

In situ spectroscopic techniques are not likely to be of value, then, in the analysis of samples of unknown composition. If known amounts of additive can be incorporated into additive-free polymer, however, these techniques are likely to be extremely useful in the study of solvent extraction procedures and the study of additive ageing processes (i.e. the effects of heat, light, sterilization, radiation, etc.), since the rate of disappearance or of decay can be measured directly by the decrease in absorbance of the sample at a suitable wavelength. Luongo[18] and Drushel and Sommers[21] have described methods for putting known amounts of additives into polymer. Luongo prepares a master batch by milling a known amount of additive into the polymer and obtains standards by further milling known weights of master batch and additive-free polymer. He then hot-moulds his samples into approximately 0·25 mm thick films, either in a standard laboratory metallographic mounting press, or in a larger press between water-cooled, polished aluminium platens. Drushel and Sommers[21] prepared their standards by adding the inhibitor in hexane solution to the polymer, evaporating the resulting slurry to dryness and hot-pressing between aluminium foil. In both cases, the films are mounted in frames before spectroscopic examination.

An example is given below of a method based on direct polymer film infrared spectroscopy for the determination of the ultraviolet absorber Cyasorb UV 531 (2-hydroxy-4-n-octoxybenzophenone) at concentrations of 0·1 to 1% in unpigmented high density polyethylene. Antioxidants such as Polygard and Santonox R do not interefere in this procedure.

Apparatus

Double-beam spectrometer covering the 15–17 μ region (e.g. Grubb Parsons GS2A).
Hydraulic press with heated and water-cooled platens.
Stainless steel moulding plates (6 in. × 6 in. × $\frac{1}{8}$ in.).
Shims 0·06 cm thick (circular 1 in. diameter or rectangular 1 in. long).
Aluminium foil.
Clear plastic rule calibrated in millimetres.
Dial gauge calibrated in 0·01-mm divisions.

Procedure

PREPARATION OF SAMPLE FILM. Cover two stainless steel moulding plates with
aluminium foil and place up to six 0·06-cm thick shims on one of these. Place
approximately 0·2 g of polymer sample in the centre of each shim and carefully place

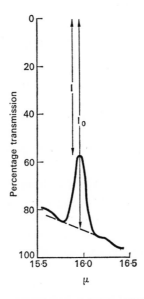

FIG. 1. Determination of UV 531 in high-
density polyethylene by direct film
infrared spectroscopy.

the second moulding plate on top. Position the two plates in the press and apply
contact pressure. Switch on the heating supply and set the thermostat to 120°C.
When the temperature reaches 120°C increase the pressure to 3000 lb/in², switch off
the heating supply and water-cool to room temperature. Carefully strip off the
aluminium foil from the polymer films and push out the films from the shims.
Check the thickness of each film by means of the dial gauge. Six readings on each
film should not vary by more than 0·03 mm. Reject any which has air bubbles, is
uneven or is wedge-shaped. Shape the film to fit the spectroscopic sample holder
and gently scrape one of the surfaces with a fine emery board to produce a series of
fine parallel lines. This reduces the incidence of interference fringes.

RECORDING THE INFRARED SPECTRUM. Place the film in the sample holder and position in the infrared instrument so that the beam passes through the film at right angles to the scratch marks.

Record the infrared spectrum from 15·5 to 16·5 μ in accord with the spectrometer operating instructions using a scanning speed of $\frac{1}{2}$ μ per minute.

Before removing the film from the instrument mark the position of the infrared beam. Remove the sample from the holder and measure the thickness to the nearest 0·01 mm by means of the dial gauge at six points within the marked area. Calculate the mean of these six measurements.

MEASUREMENT OF ABSORBANCE. Remove the chart from the spectrometer and with a sharp pencil rule a base-line from approximately 15·8 μ to approximately 16·2 μ. With a ruler measure I and I_0 to the nearest 0·1 mm at the wavelength of the peak maximum (see Fig. 1).

Calculate the absorbance at 15·94 μ and hence the absorbance per unit thickness by means of the following expression:

$$\text{Absorbance per unit thickness} = \frac{\log_{10} I_0/I}{\text{Film thickness (in cm)}}$$

CALIBRATION. Prepare duplicate films from the standard sheets containing 0·1, 0·3, 0·5 and 1·0 wt. %. UV 531 as above. Record the infrared spectrum as described above and calculate the absorbance per unit thickness as described under Measurement of absorbance. Construct a calibration curve by plotting absorbance per unit thickness against percentage weight UV 531 for each standard film. Use this calibration curve to obtain the UV 531 content of the polyethylene sample.

1.3 Preliminary Solvent Extraction of Additives from Polymer

As *in situ* methods of analysis for additives are not frequently applicable, it is necessary in most instances to use various methods, usually involving a solvent extraction procedure, for the preliminary isolation of an extract of the polymer in which is recovered a maximum amount of the additive and a minimum amount of polymer.

Discussion of Solvent Extraction Procedures

Wheeler[22] in his excellent review article has given a summary of published methods for the quantitative extraction of antioxidants from polymers prior to analysis by various techniques some of which, no doubt, could be applied equally well to other types of polymer additives.

One of the most difficult types of polymer to deal with, because of its insolubility, is the polyolefin variety. The British Standard method[29, 30] is favoured by some workers. It involves dissolution of the polymer in boiling toluene under reflux, followed by precipitation of the high molecular weight fraction with ethanol. The filtrate then contains the additives (provided these are toluene- and ethanol-soluble), plus an amount of low molecular weight polyethylene wax. Spell and Eddy,[32] however, consider this procedure too time-consuming. They have studied the extraction of the antioxidants Ionol (2,6-di-t-butyl-*p*-cresol) and Santonox (4,4′-thio-bis-(6-t-butyl-*m*-cresol)) from polyethylene, and find that the required extraction time at room temperature varies linearly with polymer density and particle size,

TABLE 1. PUBLISHED METHODS OF ANTIOXIDANT EXTRACTION

Polymer type	Substances extracted	Extracting solvent	Comments	Refs.
Polythene	Cresols Phenolic antioxidants	Chloroform	Heat at 50° for 3 hr in closed container	23
Polythene	Cresols	Hexane	Heat at 50°	24
Polythene	Antioxidants	Ether	For 24 hr in the dark at room temperature	25
Polythene	Phenolic antioxidants	Chloroform		26
Polythene	Antioxidants	Toluene	Reflux to dissolve polymer and ppte with methanol	27 28 29 30
Polythene	Antioxidants	Water	At 70° under nitrogen	31
Polythene	Phenolic antioxidants	Compares carbon disulphide with iso-octane	See text	32
Polyolefins	2,6-Di-t-butyl-p-cresol	Cyclohexane	Reflux for 30 min	33
PVC	Diphenyl thiourea 2-Phenylindole dicyandiamide	Methanol or ether		34
PVC	Stabilizers Lubricants Plasticizers	Ether		35
Rubbers	Amine and Phenolic antioxidants	Ethanol/HCl	Reflux, then steam-distil amines from extract	36
Rubbers	Phenyl salicylate Resorcinol benzoate	Ether		37
Rubbers	Antioxidants	Acetone		38 39
Rubbers	Ketone-amine condensates Phenols 2-Mercaptobenz-imidazole	Acetone		40
General	p-Phenylenedia-mine derivatives	95% Methanol or ethanol	For 16 hr in an extraction cup	41

and also with the nature of the extraction solvent. They conclude that if the polyethylene is powdered to 50 mesh, 3 hr shaking in a wrist action shaker is sufficient to recover 98% of either of the above additives from polymer of any density, i.e. between high and low density polyethylene. In support of these findings some correlation has been found between the density of polyethylene and its permeability to solvents.[42, 43]

Chloroform is a useful solvent for the quantitative extraction of additives from polyolefins. The experimental technique is illustrated below by means of an example involving the determination of Tinuvin 326 in natural or pigmented polypropylene.

Determination of Tinuvin 326 in Polypropylene

The Tinuvin 326 is extracted from the polymer with chloroform under reflux conditions. The concentration of Tinuvin 326 in the chloroform extract is determined by measuring the ultraviolet absorption peak at 355 mμ and by reference to a prepared calibration curve.

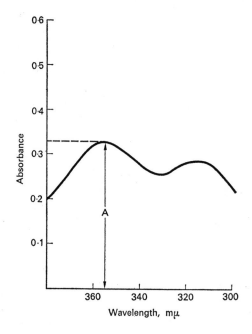

FIG. 2. Determination of Tinuvin 326 polypropylene by ultraviolet spectroscopy.

Apparatus

Ultraviolet spectrophotometer, recording type. Sample cells, quartz—1 cm path length.
Water bath.
Miscellaneous glassware.

Reagents

(a) Chloroform AR.
(b) Tinuvin 326.

Procedure

CALIBRATION. Dilute the 0·20% w/v chloroform solution of Tinuvin 326 to obtain solutions of 0·001, 0·0008, 0·0004, 0·0002% w/v.

Record the ultraviolet spectrum of each of these solutions against a chloroform blank from 300 mμ to 380 mμ using 1 cm cells. Measure the absorbance of the absorption peak at 355 mμ as shown in Fig. 2. Plot a calibration curve of absorbance against concentration of Tinuvin 326 in chloroform.

POLYMER EXTRACTION. Weigh accurately into a 250-ml round-bottomed flask a portion of the polypropylene sample, containing about 5 mg Tinuvin 326. Add 50 ml of chloroform, place the flask under a water-filled reflux condenser, bring the mixture gently to the boil on a water bath and heat for 30 min. Allow the solution to cool and decant into a 100-ml volumetric flask after filtering through a No. 42 Whatman filter paper. Transfer any polymer collected in the filter paper to the round-bottomed flask and add 40 ml of chloroform. Repeat the extraction procedure. Filter the cooled solution into the volumetric flask containing the first extract. Wash the residue with a little more chloroform, filter into the volumetric flask and make up to the 100-ml mark with chloroform. Shake the solution well and then pipette 5 ml into a 50-ml volumetric flask and make up to the mark with chloroform.

Record the ultraviolet spectrum of the diluted chloroform extract from 300 mμ to 380 mμ against a chloroform blank using 1 cm cells.

Measure the absorbance of the Tinuvin 326 absorption peak at 355 mμ (Fig. 2). Determine the amount of Tinuvin 326 present in the diluted extract by reference to a prepared calibration curve.

$$\% \text{ w/w Tinuvin 326 in polymer} = \frac{(\% \text{ w/w Tinuvin 326 in diluted extract}) \times 1000}{\text{Weight of original polymer}}$$

It must be concluded that, apart from the work of Spell and Eddy,[32] no thorough systematic investigation into the problems of quantitative extraction have been reported, although undoubtedly unreported work on this topic must have been carried out in various laboratories. With the single exception discussed below, no real attempts to minimize the decomposition and loss of sample during extraction seem to have been made, although such losses have been reported.[17, 26] On the contrary, it seems probable that many of the recommended procedures involving prolonged heating would considerably speed up the rate of decomposition and aerial oxidation unless stringent precautions are taken by use of, for example, an inert gas atmosphere during the extraction process. In this connection Crompton[44] in a method for the determination of Nonox CI (N,N-di-β-naphthyl-p-phenylenediamine) in high density polyethylene describes a 1½ hr toluene extraction of the polymer under reflux, performed under a nitrogen blanket and mentions that, under these conditions no oxidation of the antioxidant occurs. In this way he was able to distinguish between true Nonox CI oxidation occurring during polymer manufacture and "accidental" oxidation occurring during the preliminary solvent extraction stage of analysis. He also mentions that, under these conditions, some 5% of the additive remains unextracted in the polymer, but that this is allowed for in the method of calibration which involves refluxing known quantities of Nonox CI with virgin polyethylene, as in the sample extraction procedure. Robertson[72] has discussed in detail the quantitative solvent extraction of various types of plasticizers from PVC. This is discussed further in Section 1.6.

Other extraction apparatus described include Soxhlet and related extractors,[41] tightly capped bottles in which sample and solvent are heated under pressure,[21] Wiley extractors,[33] and flasks in which the sample is merely steeped in solvent.[25] In order to increase the efficiency of extraction, surfactants and ultrasonic devices have been used.[45] Attempts to increase the polymer surface-area/weight ratio before extraction have included the use of ball mills and Wiley cutting mills,[23, 26, 33] microtomes[46] and grinding with solid carbon dioxide.[34]

Yushkevichyute and Shlyapnikov[47] describe an apparatus for sublimation-distillation *in vacuo* of several antioxidants from polyethylene. Using sublimation temperatures of 61–100°C they were able to achieve satisfactory separation from polymers with molecular weights up to 50,000. In a later publication[31] they report the extractive separation of certain antioxidants from polyethylenes with distilled water at 75° under nitrogen.

1.4 Determination of Phenolic Antioxidants

A very popular method of estimating antioxidants in polymer extracts is by coupling or oxidizing them to form coloured products and measuring the resulting absorbance in the visible region of the spectrum. This technique is not particularly specific for individual antioxidants, but is specific for phenolic antioxidants in general (also amine antioxidants, see Section 1.5), and hence can often be applied without interference from other types of polymer additives.

Mayer[13] has described a quantitative method for estimating butylated hydroxy toluene (B.H.T.) involving a colour-forming reaction with 2,6-dichloro-*p*-benzoquinone-4-chloramine. Glavind[14] and Blois[15] have devised methods for estimating total antioxidants, irrespective of type, by coupling them with the free radical α,α'-diphenyl-β-picryl hydrazyl. The decrease in absorption of the reagent solution upon mixing with the polymer extract is related to the amount of antioxidant present.

Stafford[11] has described a procedure for the determination of Ionol, (2,6-di-tert-butyl-*p*-cresol), in polyolefins, involving refluxing the polymer with cyclohexane for 30 min followed by oxidation in potassium hydroxide-saturated isopropanol to produce a colour which is evaluated spectroscopically. A similar method has been described by Berger[12] for the determination of butylated hydroxy toluene (B.H.T.).

A British Standard method[10] for estimating the total phenolic antioxidant content of polyethylene involves a preliminary extraction of the polymer with hot toluene to extract the additive, followed by addition of ethanol to precipitate any dissolved polymer, then coupling the extract with diazotized sulphanilic acid to produce a colour which can be compared with standards by visible spectrophotometry. Di-cresylol propane and Santonox R (4,4′-thio-bis-(3-methyl-6-tert-butyl phenol)), in particular, are mentioned as additives that can be determined by this technique.

Metcalf and Tomlinson[8] have described a very useful general colorimetric procedure for the determination of phenolic and other types of antioxidant in polyethylenes. This procedure involves oxidation of the antioxidant (A) under controlled conditions with an absolute ethanol solution of ferric chloride:

$$A \text{ reduced} + Fe^{3+} = A \text{ oxidized} + Fe^{2+}$$

followed by reaction of the ferrous iron produced with 2,2′-dipyridyl to form a coloured complex, the intensity of which is proportional to the concentration of antioxidant present. The procedure has been applied to various phenolic and amine type antioxidants, viz. Succanox 18, butylated hydroxy toluene, Ionol (2,6-di-tert-butyl-*p*-cresol), and Nonox CI (N,N-di-β-naphthyl-*p*-phenylenediamine). A typical application of the procedure is given below, viz. to the determination of down to 0·01% of Santonox R (4,4′-thio-bis-3-methyl-6-tert-butyl phenol) in polyethylene. As the Metcalf and Tomlinson procedure determines Santonox R only in its reduced form, it does not include any Santonox R which may be present in the oxidized form in the original polymer, for example produced by atmospheric oxidation of the additive during polymer processing at elevated temperatures. Total reduced plus oxidized Santonox R can be determined by ultraviolet spectroscopic procedures, for example, the Wexler difference procedure described later, and oxidized Santonox can then be obtained by difference from the two methods. Alternatively, total unoxidized plus oxidized Santonox R can be determined by the direct ultraviolet spectroscopy as described later.

Metcalf and Tomlinson Method

Apparatus
Miscellaneous glassware. Round-bottomed flasks 100 ml, vertical condensers, volumetric flasks 100 ml and 10 ml (black painted), pipettes 25 ml and 1 ml, filter funnel 3 in. diameter.
Spectrophotometer. Unicam SP 600 or equivalent instrument.
Water bath thermostatted at $25 \pm 0.5°C$.

Reagents
Toluene, "Analar" redistilled.
Ethanol, Absolute.
2,2'-dipyridyl, 0.5%: dissolve 0.5 g 2,2'-dipyridyl in 100 ml absolute alcohol.
Ferric chloride 0.2%: dissolve 0.2 g ferric chloride hexahydrate "Analar" in 100 ml absolute ethanol. To avoid photochemical reduction of this reagent by sunlight, store in an amber glass bottle which is covered with black paper. Renew the reagent daily.

Procedure
Accurately weigh into a 100-ml round-bottomed flask 1 g of the polyethylene sample (for samples containing 0.03% or more of Santonox). If the sample contains less than 0.03% Santonox then use 2 g sample for analysis. Into the flask pipette 25 ml toluene (Note 2) and connect the flask to a vertical condenser. Heat for 90 min on a boiling water bath with occasional swirling. Low density (i.e. high pressure) polyethylenes usually completely dissolve during the reflux. High density polyethylenes (i.e. Zeigler low pressure) either completely dissolve or disperse sufficiently to allow full extraction of Santonox into the solvent phase.
Whilst the toluene solution is still hot pour 25–30 ml absolute ethanol down the condenser to precipitate dissolved polyethylene. Leave the flask to cool, stopper and shake well (refilter if the solution in the volumetric flask is cloudy). Wash the filter paper and polymer with absolute ethanol into the 100-ml volumetric flask until the liquid level reaches the 100-ml mark. Shake the flask contents well.
In a thermostatted ($25 \pm 0.5°C$) water bath clamp two dry 10-ml volumetric flasks painted with several layers of black paint (Note 3). Ensure that the flasks are almost completely immersed in water. In one flask pipette 10 ml of the polyethylene extraction solution (sample flask). Into the other flask pipette 10 ml 25–75 (v/v) toluene: absolute ethanol.
Into each flask pipette 0.5 ml of dipyridyl reagent and then 1.0 ml of ferric chloride reagent. Start a stopwatch, stopper both flasks and mix well. To facilitate the timing of the subsequent 1 hr reaction period ensure that these two reagents are added to

both flasks and the flasks are mixed and immersed in the water bath within a maximum period of 30 sec.

After 57 min remove both flasks from the water bath and pour into two 1-cm glass spectrophotometer cells (avoiding exposure to direct light as much as possible) and transfer the two cells to the spectrophotometer. Measure the optical density of the sample solution against the blank solution (in the comparison cell) at 60 ± 1 min after starting the stopwatch. Evaluate the solutions under the following spectrophotometric conditions.

Instrument. Unicam SP 600 spectrophotometer or equivalent instrument.

Cells. 1 cm glass.

Blank solution. Fill comparison cell with reagent blank as referred to in text.

Wavelength. 520 mμ.

Temperature. $25 \pm 0.5°C$.

If an optical density of greater than 0·6 is obtained then repeat the analysis. Suitably dilute the 100 ml 25:75 v/v toluene:ethanol extract of the polyethylene sample with 25:75 toluene:ethanol. Take a 10-ml portion of this diluted solution and develop the colour as described under Procedure.

CALIBRATION OF METHOD. Weigh out accurately 0·03 g Santonox R into a 100 ml volumetric flask. Make up to the 100 ml mark with 25:75 v/v toluene:absolute ethanol and shake thoroughly to completely dissolve the solid (using a warm water bath to assist solution if necessary). Pipette 5 ml of this solution into a further 100 ml volumetric flask and make up to 100 ml with 25:75 v/v toluene:ethanol. This solution contains 0·015 mg/ml Santonox R. Into two black painted 10 ml volumetric flasks immersed in a thermostatted ($25 \pm 0.5°C$) water bath pipette the volumes of blank and 0·015 mg/ml Santonox solution and the volumes of 25:75 v/v toluene:ethanol solvent mixture as shown below. Proceed with the colour development and measurement of optical density as described above. In order to facilitate the timing of the 1 hr reaction period evaluate separately each of the standard Santonox solutions. Prepare a fresh blank solution each time. To prepare a calibration graph plot optical density against the corresponding weights of Santonox R present in the 10 ml volumetric flask.

Volume of 0·015 mg/ml Santonox solution		Volume of 25:75 v/v toluene:ethanol	Weight of Santonox mg
1.	0 (blank)	10	0·00
2.	2	8	0·03
3.	4	6	0·06
4.	6	4	0·09
5.	8	2	0·12
6.	10	0	0.15

Calculations

Convert the optical density obtained from the polyethylene extract to milligram Santonox R by means of the calibration graph. Calculate the Santonox R content of the polyethylene as follows:

$$\text{Santonox R } (\% \text{ w/w}) = \frac{1000 \, N}{W}$$

N = weight (g) of Santonox R in 10 ml polyethylene extract obtained by referring determined optical density to the calibration graph,

W = weight (g) of polyethylene sample taken for analysis.

Note 1. Compounds which interfere in the 2,2′-dipyridyl/ferric chloride method.

The following compounds are known to interfere in the procedure for determining Santonox R. The described method may, indeed, be used to determine these substances in polyethylene.

Succonox 18	N-stearoyl-p-amino phenol
B.H.T.	Butylated hydroxy toluene
D.C.P.	Di-cresylol propane
Ionol	2,6-di-tert-butyl-p-cresol
Nonox CI	N,N′-di-β-naphthyl-p-phenylenediamine

Compounds used as light stabilizers in polyolefins do not usually interefere in the described procedure as they are not capable of reducing iron to the ferrous state.

Note 2. Composition of solvent in which colour development is carried out.

In the procedure recommended by Metcalf and Tomlinson[8] the polyethylene sample is heated with 10 ml toluene and then made up to 100 ml with ethanol (i.e. final solution contains 10% ethanol). This procedure was applied to some polyethylene samples and gave lower Santonox R contents than expected.

The Metcalf procedure was modified by refluxing the polyethylene with 25 ml toluene and making up to 100 ml with ethanol (i.e. 25% toluene in final extract instead of 10% toluene as in the Metcalf method). Refluxing the sample with 25 ml toluene instead of 10 ml helped in achieving a more quantitative extraction of Santonox R from low density polyethylene during the extraction.

Note 3. Photochemical reduction of ferric chloride reagent.

Alcoholic solutions of ferric chloride are reduced photochemically at quite an appreciable rate upon exposure to daylight. Reaction of the polyethylene extract with ferric chloride and 2,2′-dipyridyl reagents is carried out, therefore, in black painted volumetric flasks. These flasks should be given several layers of black paint to completely exclude daylight. The ferric chloride reagent bottle must also be protected from daylight.

During transfer from the volumetric flasks to the spectrophotometer cells, test solutions should be exposed to daylight for a minimum period of time.

In 1960 Hilton[5] published a method for the determination of phenolic antioxidants in polymers[1-4] based on the preparation of a methanol or ethanol extract of the polymer, followed by coupling the extracted phenol with diazotized p-nitroaniline in strongly acidic medium. The solution is then made alkaline and the visible absorption spectrum determined. Many of the antioxidants studied have an absorption maximum at a characteristic wavelength. Hence, in some instances, it was possible to both identify and determine the antioxidant, provided a pure specimen of the compound in question is available for calibration purposes. Table 2 shows absorptivity and wavelength maxima data taken from Hilton's paper. The method is summarized below.

TABLE 2. COMPOSITION AND ABSORPTIVITY DATA FOR PHENOLIC ANTIOXIDANTS
AFTER HILTON[5]

Antioxidant	Composition	Absorptivity A max.–A 700	Wavelength max., mμ
AgeRite Alba	Hydroquinone monobenzyl ether	31·48	565
AgeRite Spar	Styrenated phenol	44·06	548
AgeRite Superlite	A polyalkyl polyphenol	23·40	560
Antioxidant 5	Not disclosed	18·81	585
Antioxidant 425	2,2′-Methylene-bis-(6-tert-butyl-4-methyl phenol)	22·30	585
Antioxidant 2246	2,2′-Methylene-bis-(6-tert-butyl-4-methyl phenol)	20·60	578
Deenax	2,6,-Di-tert-butyl-p-cresol	Does not couple	
Ionol	2,6-Di-tert-butyl-p-cresol	Does not couple	
1-Naphthol	1-Naphthol	120·2	598
2-Naphthol	2-Naphthol	115·1	540
Naugawhite	Alkylated phenol	8·20	580
Nevastain A	Not disclosed	12·44	550
Nevastain B	Not disclosed	6·62	550
Nonyl phenol	Nonyl phenol	36·25	538
p-Phenyl phenol	p-Phenyl phenol	80·80	548
Polygard	Tris (nonylated phenyl) phosphite	Must be hydrolysed before it will couple	
Santovar A	2,5-Di-tert-amyl-hydroquinone	Colour too weak	
Santovar O	2,5-Di-tert-butyl-hydroquinone	Colour too weak	
Santowhite Crystals	4,4′-Thio-bis-(6-tert-butyl-2-methyl phenol)	78·84	565
Santowhite MK	Reaction product of 6-tert-butyl-m-cresol and SCl$_2$	66·94	560
Santowhite Powder	4,4′-Butylidene-bis (3-methyl-6-tert-butyl phenol)	Colour too weak	
Solux	N-p-Hydroxyphenyl-morpholine	Colour too weak	
Stabilite white powder	Not disclosed	Colour too weak	
Styphen I	Styrenated phenol	22·61	558
Wingstay S	Styrenated phenol	50·82	545
Wingstay T	A hindered phenol	10·27	590

Reagents

Ethyl alcohol, 95%. Sodium hydroxide pellets, reagent grade, 4N; 160 g of sodium hydroxide per litre (distilled water).

p-Nitroaniline, Matheson Coleman and Bell, melting point 146–147°C.

Sodium nitrite, Baker's Analyst Reagent grade.

Coupling agent, 2·800 g of p-nitroaniline dissolved in 10 ml of hot concentrated hydrochloric acid and diluted with water to 250 ml. After cooling to room temperature, the volume of liquid is adjusted to exactly 250 ml. A second solution is made containing 1·44 g sodium nitrite in exactly 250 ml of distilled water. Both of the above solutions are reputed to be stable indefinitely.

Twenty-five millilitres of each of these solutions are pipetted into separate 100-ml beakers and are chilled in ice to below 10°C. The contents are mixed by combining the solutions and pouring them back and forth from one beaker to the other. Pure nitrogen is bubbled through the mixture as it is allowed to warm to room temperature. Finally, add 10 mg urea to destroy excess nitrous acid.

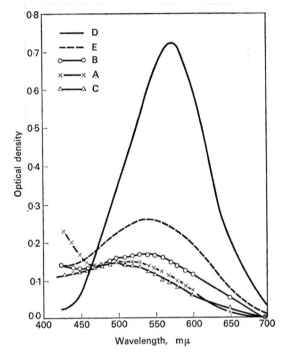

FIG. 3. Comparison of absorption spectra of diazotized *p*-nitroaniline coupled extracts from 0·3 g high impact polystyrenes.

Procedure

The sample to be analysed must be very thinly sheeted or powdered. A 2·000 ± 0·020 g sample is accurately weighed and wrapped with extraction cloth which has been previously extracted to remove sizing, etc. The sample is placed in an Underwriter's extraction cup and extracted for 16 hr with 95% ethanol or methanol. The alcohol extract is transferred to a 100-ml volumetric flask, cooled to room temperature, and brought to the mark with the extraction solvent. A 10-ml aliquot is transferred to a 100-ml volumetric flask. Two millilitres of coupling reagent are added. The solution is thoroughly mixed and 3 ml of 4N sodium hydroxide solution are added. The solution is then brought to the mark with 95% ethanol or methanol. (The sample weight, the size of the aliquot, or both may be adjusted to give a more satisfactory colour. However, the total volume at the time of adding the coupling solution must be 10 ml.)

The absorption spectrum from 700 to 400 mμ is determined using a suitable spectrophotometer with quartz cells. The colour formation is complete by the time the solution is brought to the mark and is stable for at least 2 hr. Ethyl alcohol is used

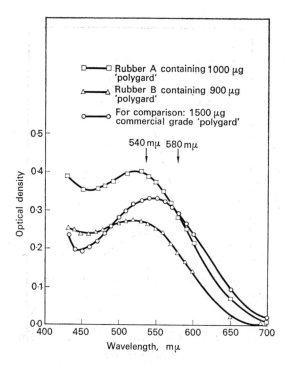

FIG. 4. Comparison of absorption spectra of coupled "Polygard" impurity and extracts of 0·1 g of synthetic rubbers A and B.

in the reference cell unless the alcohol extract is strongly coloured. In this case, the reference solvent is taken to be a 10-ml aliquot of the ethyl alcohol extract diluted to 100 ml with ethyl alcohol. The absorbance readings are plotted on semilogarithmic graph paper. The per cent antioxidant is calculated using the equation developed for the antioxidant concerned.

Figure 3 shows absorption spectra in the 400–700 mμ region of solvent extracts of five polystyrenes obtained by coupling with diazotized p-nitroaniline. Only polystyrene D shows clear evidence for the presence of a phenolic antioxidant—as is evidenced by the formation of a blue-violet coloration upon addition of the reagent.

Figures 4 and 5 show the absorption spectra obtained upon coupling extracts of various styrene–butadiene rubbers.

The spectra of rubbers A and B (Fig. 4) are due to the presence in the rubber of nonyl phenol present as an impurity or decomposition product in the Polygard (tris (nonylated phenyl) phospite) additive present in these rubbers. The phosphorus contents of these polymers indicated that they contained about 1% Polygard (Table 3). Rubbers C and D (Fig. 5) did not contain Polygard but did contain a phenolic antioxidant.

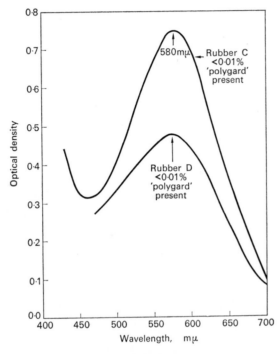

FIG. 5. Absorption spectra of diazotized *p*-nitroaniline coupled extracts from 0·1 g styrene–butadiene rubbers C and D.

Straightforward ultraviolet spectroscopy is liable to be in error owing to intereference by other highly absorbing impurities that may be present in the sample.[315–318] Interference by such impurities in direct ultraviolet spectroscopy has been overcome or minimized by selective solvent extraction or by chromatography.[316] However, within prescribed limits ultraviolet spectroscopy is of use and, as an example, procedures are described below for the determination of Ionol (2,6-di-tert-butyl-*p*-cresol) and of Santonox R (4,4'-thio-bis-6-tert-butyl-*m*-cresol) in polyolefins.

Certain additives, e.g. calcium stearate and dilauryl thio-dipropionate, do not interfere in the determination. Other phenolic antioxidants, e.g. Ionox 330, Topanol CA and Santonox R, do interfere.

TABLE 3. "POLYGARD" AND PHENOLIC-TYPE ANTIOXIDANTS IN SYNTHETIC STYRENE–
BUTADIENE RUBBER SAMPLES

| Sample description | "Polygard"* % w/w | p-Nitroaniline test for phenolic antioxidants | | Comments |
| | | Optical densities obtained upon adding coupling reagent to solvent extract from 0·1 g of rubber | | |
		at 540 mμ	at 580 mμ	
A	0·9	0·23	0·17	Maximum absorption at 530–540 mμ (i.e. "Polygard" impurities)
B	1·0	0·40	0·28	Maximum absorption at 530–540 mμ (i.e. "Polygard" impurities)
C	Nil	0·72	0·94	Maximum absorption at approx. 580 mμ. Phenolic present. No peak at 540 mμ.
D	Nil	0·40	0·48	Maximum absorption at approx. 580 mμ. Phenolic present. No peak at 540 mμ.

* Calculated from phosphorus content of rubber.

Determination of Ionol Antioxidant in Polyolefins

Apparatus

Ultraviolet spectrophotometer, recording type.
Sample cells, quartz—1 cm path length.
Miscellaneous glassware.
Heating mantle, electrical, 250 ml capacity, with variable control.

Reagents

Chloroform—AR.
Ionol CP—dried by vacuum desiccation for 4 hr before use.

Procedure

CALIBRATION. Make up accurately a 0·05% w/v solution of Ionol CP in 250 ml chloroform.
Dilute this stock solution to obtain Ionol CP solutions of 0·025, 0·02, 0·01, 0·005% w/v.

Record the ultraviolet spectrum of each of the above solutions against a chloroform blank from 250 to 310 mμ using 1-cm cells. Measure the absorbance of the absorption peak at 278 mμ by drawing a base-line from approximately 260 to 300 mμ as shown in Fig. 6.

Plot a calibration curve of absorbance against concentration of Ionol CP in chloroform.

EXTRACTION. Weigh 20·0 g of polymer sample into a 250-ml round-bottomed flask and add 50 ml of chloroform. Connect the water-cooled condenser, place on the electric heating mantle and bring gently to boiling point. Reflux for 30 min at a moderate rate. Allow to cool and then carefully decant the chloroform solution into a 100-ml volumetric flask (using a filter if necessary) and stopper immediately. Add a further 40 ml of chloroform to the round-bottomed flask and carry out a second extraction of the polymer. When cool, filter the contents into the volumetric flask containing the first extract. Wash the residue with sufficient chloroform to make up to the mark. Shake the flask to ensure homogeneity.

Record the ultraviolet spectrum of the chloroform extract against a chloroform blank from 250 to 310 mμ using 1-cm cells.

Measure the absorbance of the Ionol CP absorption peak at 278 mμ (see Fig. 6). Determine the concentration of Ionol CP present in the extract by reference to the prepared calibration curve.

Calculation

Calculate the concentration of Ionol CP present in the polymer by means of the following expression:

% w/w Ionol CP in polymer = 5 × (% w/v Ionol CP in chloroform extract).

Determination of Santonox R Antioxidant in Polyolefins

Outline

Santonox R is extracted from a finely ground sample with boiling cyclohexane. The extract is then shaken with aqueous sodium hydroxide. Santonox R forms a sodium salt in the alkali layer. This layer is then examined on an ultraviolet spectrophotometer. The base line absorbance is calculated and referred to a previously calibrated graph of Santonox R versus base line absorbance. Ionol CP does not interefere in the determination.

Apparatus

Apex Mill.
Spectrophotometer.
Water bath.
1-cm silica cells.
50-ml standard flasks.
100-ml standard flasks.
1000-ml standard flask.
100-ml R.B. flasks with ground glass neck.
Condensers with ground glass neck.
Filter funnels.
5: 10: 20 ml pipettes.
25-ml graduated cylinders.
Filter paper: Green's No. 802 or similar.

Reagents

Santonox R, 4,4′-thio-bis-(6-tert-butyl-3-methylphenol).

Cyclohexane—spectroscopic grade.

Sodium hydroxide pellets—Analar.

PREPARATION OF REAGENTS. Standard Santonox R solution: dissolve 0·1000 g Santonox R in cyclohexane in a 1000-ml standard flask and dilute to graduation mark. Sodium hydroxide solution: dissolve 42 g sodium hydroxide pellets in distilled water and make up to 1000 ml.

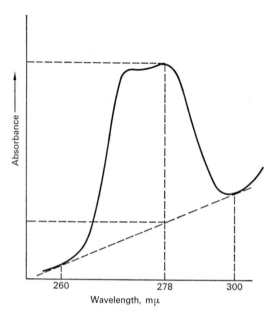

FIG. 6. Determination of Ionol CP in polyolefins by ultraviolet spectroscopy.

CALIBRATION. Put accurately measured portions of 5, 10, 15 and 20 ml standard Santonox R solution into 50-ml standard flasks and dilute to graduation mark. Transfer each into a 100-ml separating funnel and add 25 ml freshly prepared sodium hydroxide solution. Shake for 3 min, allow to settle, then run the lower layer into a 100-ml standard flask. Repeat the extraction with another 2×25 ml portions of alkali. Make up the volume to 100 ml and mix thoroughly. Read against sodium hydroxide in 1-cm silica cells at the following wavelengths—335, 266, 236 mμ. Calculate the base line absorbance from the following equation:

$$A_{BL} = A_{266} - A_{335} - 0.684 \, (A_{236} - A_{335})$$

where A_{BL} = base line absorbance,

$A_{335}, A_{266}, A_{236}$ = absorbance at 335, 266, 236 mμ respectively.

Plot the base line absorbance against the concentration of Santonox R in mg/100 ml.

ANALYSIS OF SAMPLE. Grind a representative sample in the Apex Mill. Weigh about 1 g of the sample into a 100 ml round-bottomed flask and add 20 ml cyclohexane. Fit a condenser to the flask and allow the cyclohexane to reflux on a water bath for 1 hr. Wash down the condenser with 20 ml cyclohexane, remove the flask from the bath, cool to room temperature and shake well. Filter through a No. 802 filter paper into a 100-ml separating funnel. Wash the filter paper with a further 10 ml cyclohexane. Add 25 ml freshly prepared sodium hydroxide solution, shake for 3 min then allow to settle. Run off the caustic layer into a 100-ml standard flask. Repeat the extraction with another 2×25 ml portions of alkali, make the extract up to 100 ml, mix thoroughly and record the optical densities at 335, 266, 236 mμ using 1-cm silica cells and sodium hydroxide solution as a blank. Calculate the base line absorbance as stated in the calibration procedure and read the concentration of Santonox R from the graph.

Calculate the Santonox R content as follows:

$$\text{Weight \% Santonox R} = \frac{B}{10W}$$

where B = Santonox R content of extract in mg/100 ml,
W = weight of sample (g).

Note 1. The optical density of the cyclohexane should not exceed 0·15 at 247 mμ.

Note 2. The sodium hydroxide must be Analar- and carbonate-free. Carbonate adhering to the pellets may be removed by washing the pellets with distilled water.

In an attempt to overcome the difficulty of interference effects by other polymer additives in the ultraviolet spectroscopic determination of phenolic antioxidants Wexler[7] makes use of the bathochromic shift exhibited by phenols on changing from a neutral or acidic medium to an alkaline one. This shift is due to the change of absorbing species because of solute–solvent interaction. Using a double-beam recording spectrophotometer, he measured a difference spectrum by placing an alkaline solution of the polymer extract in the sample beam, and an identical concentration of sample in acid solution in the reference beam. The resulting difference spectrum is a characteristic and useful indication of the concentration and chemical identity of the phenolic substance. Possible interferences due to non-ionizing, non-phenolic species are usually cancelled out in the difference spectrum which should make the technique of interest to the polymer analyst. Typical spectra obtained for an antioxidant are shown in Figs. 7 and 8. Each spectrum exhibits two maxima and two minima. Close adherence to Beer's law is usually obeyed by the difference peak spectra.

Wexler studied the following compounds:
p-methoxy phenol, 4,4'-methylene-bis-(2,6-di-tert-butyl phenol), and
Santonox R (4,4'-thio-bis-(6-tert-butyl-m-cresol)).

Scheele and his co-workers[48, 49] have found extensive agreement between conductiometric and ultraviolet spectroscopic methods of quantitative antioxidant analysis.

Spell and Eddy[6] have described infrared spectroscopic procedures for the determination of up to 500 ppm of various additives in polyethylene pellets following solvent extraction of additives at room temperature. They showed that Ionol (2,6-di-t-butyl-p-cresol) and Santonox R (4,4'-thio-bis-(6-t-butyl-m-cresol) are extracted quantitatively from polyethylene pellets by carbon disulphide in 2–3 hr and by iso-octane in 50–75 hr. The carbon disulphide extract is suitable for scanning in the infrared region between 7·8 and 9·3 μ, whilst the iso-octane extract is suitable for scanning between 250 and 350 mμ.

In many instances visible fluorescence techniques are less subject to interference by other polymer additives present in a polymer extract than are ultraviolet methods of analysis. Therefore, in some instances visible fluorimetry offers a method of determining a polymer

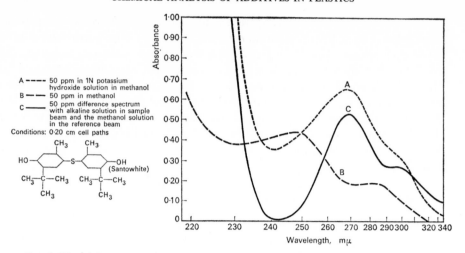

FIG. 7. Ultraviolet spectra of 4,4'- thio-bis-(6-tert-butyl-*m*-cresol) exhibiting bathochromic shift in alkaline medium after Wexler[7].

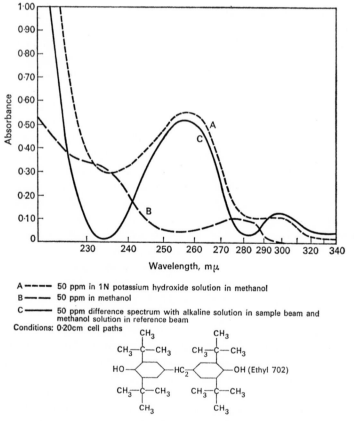

FIG. 8. Ultraviolet spectra of 4,4'-methylene bis-(2,6-di-tert-butyl phenol) exhibiting bathochromic shift in alkaline medium after Wexler[7].

constituent without interference from other constituent, when this would not be possible by ultraviolet spectroscopy. Apart from specificity, fluorescence techniques are more sensitive than absorption spectroscopic techniques. It is noteworthy that in this connection Drushel and Sommers[21] have discussed the determination of Age Rite D (polymeric dihydroxy quinone) and phenyl-2-naphthylamine in polymers by fluorescence methods and Santonox R (4,4'-thio-bis-(6-tert-butyl-*m*-cresol)) and phenyl-2-naphthylamine by phosphorescence methods. They emphasize the freedom that such techniques have from interference by other polymer additives and polymerization catalyst residues.

Aromatic amines and phenols are among the few classes of compounds in which a large proportion of their members exhibit sensible fluorescence; other types of visible fluorescing compounds include some hydroxy benzoquinones, hydroxy methoxy benzophenones and coumarin derivatives (see Section 1.7 on ultraviolet absorbers used in polymer formulations). Parker and Barnes[329] found that in solvent extracts of rubbers the strong absorption by pine-tar and other constituents masks the absorption spectra of phenyl naphthylamines, whereas the fluorescence spectra of these amines are sufficiently unaffected for them to be determined directly in the unmodified extract by the fluorescence method. In a later paper[330] Parker discussed the possibility of using phosphorescence techniques for determining phenyl-naphthylamines.

Numerous titrimetric methods have been described for the assay of phenolic antioxidants in the 1–200 mg range. Thus phenolics have been estimated by non-aqueous titration with a standard solution of sodium isopropoxide in pyridine medium[50] using a potentiometric or conductiometric end-point.

Schröder and Rudolph[26] determine phenolic antioxidants by treating the polymer extract with potassium bromide/potassium bromate and estimating the unconsumed bromide by sodium thiosulphate titration. This method requires less than 1 mg of antioxidant. They applied this method to seven antioxidants, including 2-tert-butyl-4-methyl phenol, 2',6-di-tert-butyl-4-methyl-phenol, *p*-tert-butyl phenol, and 2,2'-bis-(4-methyl-6-tert-butyl phenyl) methane.

Morgenthaler[9] has described a further procedure involving potassium bromide and bromate for the estimation of Santonox R in polyethylene.

He claims that his method is applicable to the determination of antioxidants after the partial degradation of the polymer either by heat or beta-irradiation, both of which are likely to cause large indeterminate errors in the analyses in methods based on diazotization coupling reactions to produce coloured products (where oxidation products of the antioxidant are the cause of the interference), and based on ultraviolet absorption methods (where background absorption increases occur due to irradiation of polyethylene). He investigated several oxidizing agents in an effort to analyse the antioxidant, and found that acidic bromate ion was a suitable reagent.

Reagents

Potassium bromate, 0·1N: dissolve 2·783 g of reagent grade $KBrO_3$, dried at 150°C, in a small quantity of water and dilute with water to 1 l.

Santonox R obtained from Monsanto Chemical Company, recrystallized from benzene and benzene removed by heating the crystals for 2 hr at 100°C, m.p. = 161°, was used for standardization.

All other materials were reagent grade.

Procedure

Mill or slice into thin sections a sample containing from 10 to 30 mg of Santonox and weigh into a 250 ml boiling flask. Fit the flask with a reflux condenser, add 100 ml of reagent grade methanol and reflux for 24 hr. Decant the methanol and rinse the flask and its contents several times with small quantities of methanol. Transfer the combined rinses and solvent to a titration vessel and add 10 ml of 1 M aqueous sulphuric acid, one or two crystals of potassium bromide and a few drops of methyl red solution. Stir vigorously with a magnetic stirrer while titrant is added at a rate of about one drop every 3 sec. As the end-point is approached, a slight fading begins to occur. Then add the titrant dropwise, allowing complete reaction of each drop before further addition. The use of larger samples or more dilute titrant renders the endpoint quite indistinct (optimum titrant volume added 2–8 ml).

Weight mg of Santonox titrated = 4·11 × volume of titrant (accuracy of better than 2% of the total Santonox present).

Table 4 gives values obtained in the determination of the titre of Santonox. Values of comparable precision were obtained for all of the determinations performed.

TABLE 4. STANDARDIZATION OF SANTONOX BY
POTASSIUM BROMATE PROCEDURE

Weight of Santonox	Volume of Bromate	mg Santonox/ ml Titrant
21·2	5·10	4·16
30·8	7·55	4·08
19·6	4·79	4·09
20·4	5·00	4·08
26·2	6·30	4·16

Average titre = 4·11 ± 0·05 mg/ml, 95% confidence.
$s = 0.042$.

Morgenthaler investigated a number of possible sources of error. The first was the extraction of broken side chains or low molecular weight fragments of the polyethylene which might be oxidizable by the bromate or which might contain carbonyl groups that could possibly interfere with the mechanism of the indicator reaction. A low molecular weight, very highly branched polyethylene, more closely resembling paraffin in physical properties than the usual forms of polyethylene, was chosen for the examination. Samples of this material containing no stabilizer were extracted and titrated. A small and reproducible blank value corresponding to 0·4 mg of Santonox was obtained. The same procedure was followed on samples of the same material that had received approximately 20 megarads of beta-irradiation, with no increase in the value of the blank. No difference in blank value was found when the sample was heat-moulded and then sliced or when the sample was crumbled to a fine powder. The methyl alcohol extraction procedure introduced the possibility of further difficulties, in that the distribution coefficient of the antioxidant between plastic and alcohol had to be such that essentially complete separation would occur in a single extraction, without errors introduced by absorption of the antioxidant on the surface of the plastic. Three samples were prepared by weighing the unstabilized highly branched polymer into an extraction flask along with a known quantity of Santonox. The plastic was melted in the flask and stirred to provide dispersion of the antioxidant in the plastic. The flask was then cooled in ice water, and the plastic crumbled. The contents of the flask were then extracted and titrated. The results are given in Table 5.

TABLE 5. ANALYSIS OF SANTONOX–POLYETHYLENE MIXTURES BY
POTASSIUM BROMATE METHOD

mg Santonox	g Polyethylene	% Santonox (prepared)	% Santonox (found)
17·9	1·056	1·70	1·67
89·0	1·151	7·73	7·81
20·2	1·676	1·20	1·15

A further source of error investigated, was the possible oxidation of the antioxidant by exposure to atmospheric oxygen during the extraction procedure. Three samples of antioxidant were weighed out and dissolved in methanol. The solutions were then refluxed without the exclusion of air for 24 hr after which they were titrated with bromate. The results given in Table 6 indicate no oxidation during this process.

TABLE 6. POTASSIUM BROMATE PROCEDURE
Analysis of Santonox after 24 hours
Reflux in Methanol

mg Santonox weighed	mg Santonox found
10·6	10·5
23·7	23·4
40·3	40·1

Reaction products of Santonox formed from its oxidation during polymer processing were thought to be a possible source of interference. Unsaturates would interfere, but it was shown that alcohol extraction removed negligible quantities of unsaturates from the polymer. Thermal degradation of Santonox R is likely to produce sulphones and quinones. These were shown to introduce no errors in the analysis.

Electrochemical methods have been investigated, but in general are only to be recommended where a simpler method is not available. Mocker[51, 52, 53] and Mocker and Old[54] have explored the use of polarography and find the technique to be more applicable to rubber accelerators than to antioxidants. They included both phenolic and amine types of antioxidants in their study. Difficulties arise because the dropping mercury electrode cannot be used at potentials more positive than $+0.4$ V with respect to the saturated calomel electrode, and since many aromatic phenols (and amines) can only be oxidized at electrodes, positive voltages have to be applied in their analysis. Nevertheless, the polarography of some amines and phenols has been studied,[55-58] and whilst no electrode is as suitable for polarography as the dropping mercury electrode, antioxidants have also been studied with other types of electrodes, notably the graphite[59, 60, 270, 275, 278] and the platinum[61, 66] electrode. These methods include the determination by voltammetric methods of N,N'-di-sec-butyl-p-phenylenediamine and N-butyl-p-amino phenol in gasoline[275] and of Ionol (2,6-di-tert-butyl-p-cresol).[59] In addition, at least two commercially available antioxidants have been shown by differential cathode-ray polarography to exhibit reduction waves: Santonox R (4,4'-thio-bis-(3-methyl-6-t-butyl phenol)) gives a poorly shaped wave at −0·6 V in an electrolyte consisting of ammonia and ammonium chloride in methanol–water[63] and 3,5-di-t-butyl-4-hydroxytoluene gives a wave at −0·65 V in aqueous sodium or lithium hydroxide.[64] In both cases, 40 ppm of analyte gave a current which was adequate for quantitative analysis.

Other procedures which have been described include the conversion of an antioxidant into a polarographically reducible form[65] and a general method for antioxidants which involved measuring a decrease in the height of the wave, due to the reduction of dissolved oxygen by antioxidants.[66]

Ward[62] has discussed in some detail the determination of phenolic and amine types of antioxidants and antiozonants in polymers by the chronopotentiometric technique, using a paraffin wax impregnated graphite indicating electrode[273, 274] and solutions of lithium chloride and lithium perchlorate in acetonitrile and in 95% ethanol as supporting electrolytes. Precision obtainable for repeated chronopotentiometric runs in acetonitrile was found to be better than ± 1·0% in cases in which electrode fouling did not occur, and ± 1·7% when the electrode was fouled by electrolysis products.

In Table 7 are shown data obtained by Ward[62] in a chronopotentiometric study of several commercially available antioxidants.

TABLE 7. CHRONOPOTENTIOMETRY OF VARIOUS COMMERCIAL
ANTIOXIDANTS IN 95% ETHANOL

c, mmoles/	$ir^{\frac{1}{2}}/C$	Supporting electrolyte
A. 2,6-Di-t-butylcresol		
10·10	124·0	LiClO$_4$
6·06	126·0	
3·03	136·0	
1·01	152·0	
B. Age-Rite Alba: Hydroquinone monobenzyl ether		
10·10	111·0	LiCl
6·04	112·0	
3·02	122·0	
1·01	136·0	
C. Flexone 6H: N'-Phenyl-N'-cyclohexyl phenylenediamine		
9·83	84·2	LiCl
5·90	88·3	
2·95	89·8	
0·98	105·0	
D. Age-Rite Stalite: Heptylated diphenylamine		
10·00	73·2	LiCl
6·02	74·6	
3·01	80·3	
1·00	93·0	

E. Santovar A: 2,5-Di-t-amylhydroquinone

10·10	91·1	LiCl
6·06	94·0	
3·03	98·0	
1·01	107·0	

F. Flexone 3C: N-Isopropyl-N′-phenyl phenylenediamine

10·30	96·3	LiCl
6·17	99·4	
3·09	110·6	
1·03	119·3	

G. Age-Rite powder: N-Phenyl-β-naphthylamine

10·30	159·0	LiCl
6·21	157·0	
3·11	160·0	
1·03	186·0	

H. Antioxidant 2246: 2,2′-Methylene-bis-(6-t-butyl-4-ethylphenol)

10·00	237·0	LiClO$_4$
6·00	229·0	
3·00	231·0	
1·00	243·0	

I. Santowhite powder refined: 4,4′-Butylidene-bis-(3-methyl-6-t-butylphenol)

11·20	323·0	LiClO$_4$
6·73	316·0	
3·36	348·0	
1·12	410·0	

Although $ir^{\frac{1}{2}}/C$ always increased as antioxidant concentration (C) was decreased, plots of $ir^{\frac{1}{2}}$ versus C gave a nearly straight line suitable for use as an analytical working curve (Table 7).

Antioxidant concentrations are calculated on the assumption that the commercial product is greater than 95% pure, i.e. the $ir^{\frac{1}{2}}/C$ values provide a useful estimation of the range of concentration over which the method is applicable. In general, chronopotentiometry appears well suited to the determination of antioxidants in the concentration range from 10^{-4} to 10^2 M. This range places a lower limit of 0·2–0·5% by weight on the concentration of antioxidant which could be measured in actual samples, depending on the molecular weight of the antioxidant, if the antioxidant content of a 2·0-g sample is extracted into 10 ml of solution. This sensitivity, of course, may be greatly improved by procedures for increasing the sample–extractant ratio or concentration of the extract.

None of the substances studied and listed in Table 7 was found to cause electrode fouling at any concentration level.

At a given concentration of electro-active species, the product $ir^{\frac{1}{2}}$ was constant as i and thus r were varied over a 2- to 3-fold range.

The range of transition times measured was limited to not less than 5 nor more than 30 sec. The lower limit was imposed by the accuracy with which it was possible to measure r with the recorder used. The upper limit results from disturbance of the diffusion layer by such effects as vibration, convection, etc. Within these limits, the precision with which transition times could be reproduced was $\pm 1·0\%$, even when the electrode was removed from the solution between runs and dried before being replaced. This increase in reproducibility appears to rise from the ability of the solvent to wet the electrode and suggests an important advantage to be gained by the use of non-aqueous solvents with carbon electrodes.

Phenolic (and amine) antioxidants have been titrated electrometrically with lithium aluminium hydride, with platinum or silver electrodes.[67] Small amounts of water in the sample or analysis solvent have an influence on the results obtained by these procedures.

Electrophoresis is a technique worthy of further consideration for the analysis of antioxidants. Sawada et al.[311] report successful separations by coupling the antioxidants with p-diazobenzene sulphonic acid before electrophoresis. Amine antioxidants are coupled in acetic acid and phenolic antioxidants in sodium hydroxide–ethanol. Electrophoresis was carried out in 1% w/v methanolic sodium borate.

1.5 Determination of Amine Antioxidants

Hilton[68, 313] has reported an excellent procedure, described below, for the colorimetric determination of amine antioxidants.

Apparatus

All of the absorption measurements were made on a Cary Model II spectrophotometer using quartz cells having a light path of 1·000 cm. The slit widths used were as shown below.

Slit Widths Used in the Determination of Amine Antioxidants

Wavelength mμ	Slit width mm	Wavelength mμ	Slit width mm
350	0·054	550	0·006
375	0·029	575	0·006
400	0·017	600	0·008
425	0·012	625	0·012
450	0·009	650	0·018
475	0·007	675	0·027
500	0·006	700	0·043
525	0·006		

Reagents

The reagents used were:

Methanol—pure synthetic Methanol (99·85%).

Hydrochloric acid—pure laboratory reagent grade, specific gravity 1·188 (37·2% hydrochloric acid by weight).

p-Nitroaniline—micro-analytical reagent. British Drug Houses Ltd.

Sodium nitrite—reagent grade.

Coupling agent—2·800 g of p-nitroaniline is dissolved in 32 ml of hot concentrated hydrochloric acid and the solution is diluted with distilled water to 250 ml. After cooling to room temperature the volume of liquid is adjusted to exactly 250 ml. A second solution is made containing 1·44 g of sodium nitrite in exactly 250 ml of distilled water. Both of the above solutions are reputed to be stable indefinitely. Twenty-five ml of each of these solutions are pipetted into separate 100-ml beakers and are chilled in ice to below 10°C. The contents are mixed by combining the solutions and pouring back and forth from one beaker to the other. Pure nitrogen is bubbled through the mixture as it is allowed to warm to room temperature. Finally,

10 mg of urea (or 1 ml of 0·1 g/10 ml solution) is added to destroy any excess nitrous acid. The reagent becomes cloudy after an hour or so but is suitable for use for several hours. Fresh reagent should be made every day.

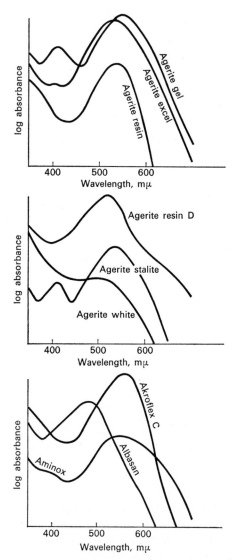

FIG. 9. Visible spectra of amine antioxidants diazotized p-nitroaniline method after Hilton.[68, 31]

Methanol–hydrochloric acid solvent. Three volumes of methanol are placed in a glass stoppered bottle and one volume of concentrated hydrochloric acid is added gradually with gentle mixing. The mixture is allowed to come to room temperature before carrying out the analyses.

Procedure "A"

The sample to be analysed must be very thinly sheeted or powdered. Weigh a 1.000 ± 0.0005 g sample. Wrap with extraction cloth which has been previously extracted to remove sizing, etc. Place in an Underwriter's extraction cup and extract for 16 hr with 95% ethanol or methanol. Transfer the alcohol extract to a 100-ml volumetric flask. Cool to room temperature and bring to the mark with the extraction solvent. Transfer a 10-ml aliquot to a 100-ml volumetric flask. Add 15 ml methanol–hydrochloric acid solution and 1 ml of coupling agent. Place in dark for $1\frac{1}{2}$ hr and then bring to the mark with methanol–hydrochloric acid. Determine the absorption spectrum from 700 mμ to 350 mμ using a Cary Spectrophotometer or other spectrophotometer (see Fig. 9).

If a red colour is formed immediately upon coupling and the colour then fades to an amber or brown, it is likely that one of the antioxidants containing phenyl-beta-naphthylamine (PBNA) is present. In this case the alternate procedure "B" must be used.

Antioxidants which can be Determined by
Procedure "A"

Agerite Excel	Flectol H
Agerite Gel	Flexamine
Agerite Resin	Neozone A
Agerite Resin D	Neozone C
Agerite Stalite	Octamine
Akroflex C	Polylite
Albasan	Stabilite
Aminox	Stabilite ALBA
Antox	Stabilite L
Aranox	Thermoflex A
Betanox†	Thermoflex C
BLE-25	VGB
BLE Powder	

† Coupled colour insoluble in methanol–hydrochloric acid. Coupled in methanol–hydrochloric acid and dilute with glacial acetic acid.

Alternate procedure "B" for PBNA

Extract as indicated in the regular procedure. Take a 10-ml aliquot from the 100-ml volumetric flask. Bring almost to the mark with methanol–hydrochloric acid mixture and add 1 ml of coupling agent. Bring exactly to the mark, mix and immediately determine the absorbance. The absorbance will rise to a maximum in 2 to 5 min

Antioxidants containing PBNA requiring
Procedure "B"

Agerite HIPAR	Neozone D
Agerite HP	PBNA
Agerite Powder	Thermoflex A
Akroflex CD	Thermoflex C

after coupling. Use this maximum absorbance in calculating the amount of antioxidant present.

The antioxidants for which methods have been found to be unsatisfactory are Agerite White, Antioxidant 4010, BXA, Eastozone 32, JZF (DPPD), OZO 88, Santoflex AW, Santoflex BX, Santoflex DD, Santoflex 35, Santoflex 75, Tenamine 2, Tenamine 30, Tonox, Tonox D, U.O.P. 88 and U.O.P. 288.

A British standard procedure[30] describes a method for the determination of Nonox CI (N,N′-di-2-naphthyl-p-phenylenediamine) in low density polyethylene. In this method the antioxidant is separated from the polymer by bringing the polyethylene into solution in toluene, followed by precipitation of the polymer with ethanol. The mixture is then filtered to remove polymer, the antioxidant remaining in the filtrate. The antioxidant content of the filtrate is determined colorimetrically by oxidation with hydrogen peroxide, in the presence of sulphuric acid. This reagent produces a green colour with Nonox CI, which gradually reaches a maximum intensity. The colour is evaluated at 430 mμ when the maximum depth of colour is reached. Crompton[44] has described a modification to this procedure for the determination of Nonox CI in high density polyethylene which, compared to low density polymer, has only a small solubility in toluene. He has also extended the procedure to the determination of oxidized Nonox CI, and a further product which he calls degraded Nonox CI. This latter material is produced only in polymers containing acidic forms of carbon black and is believed to be produced by decomposition of oxidized Nonox CI by carbon black acidity. He applied these procedures to a study of the effect of twelve different acidic and alkaline carbon blacks on Nonox CI degradation, occurring during polyethylene extrusion.

The Metcalf and Tomlinson[8] colorimetric dipyridyl procedure, already described in Section 1.4, can be applied to various amine-type antioxidants, e.g. Nonox CI and Succonox 18 (N-steoroyl-p-amino phenol).

Hilton[41] has described a colorimetric method for determining amine antioxidants (p-phenylenediamine derivatives) based on reaction of an ethanol extract of the polymer with cupric acetate in a hydrochloric acid/potassium chloride buffered medium.

Sawada[69] has described two colorimetric methods for the determination of amine antioxidants based, respectively, on reaction with benzoyl peroxide and on a coupling reaction with p-diazobenzene sulphonic acid. Glavind's[14] α,α′-diphenyl-β-picrylhydrazyl colorimetric method is also applicable to amines. Sircar[312] was able to distinguish between various p-phenylenediamine-type antioxidants by means of the colours produced with acid permanganate in ethanol, which they measured spectroscopically. Kabota[314] made coloured derivatives of amines with benzothiazolin-2-one-hydrazone-hydrochloride and ferric chloride, and evaluated the colours obtained spectroscopically.

Davies[70] was able to estimate 1–20 mg of p-phenylenediamine derivatives by visual titration in chloroform with toluene-p-sulphonic acid, using methyl orange as indicator. Lorenz and Parks[71] showed that p-phenylenediamine derivatives are oxidized by chloranil to form one equivalent of a base which is then titrated in a non-aqueous medium with standard perchloric acid.

The application of polarographic and chronopotentiometric procedures to the quantitative estimation of amine antioxidants has been discussed at the end of Section 1.4, dealing with phenolic antioxidants.

The applicability of fluorimetric and phosphorescence techniques to the determination of certain types of amines in polymer extracts is also discussed in Section 1.4.

1.6   Determination of Plasticizers

Robertson and Rowley[72] have published an excellent detailed description of methods for the solvent extraction of plasticizers from polyvinyl chloride and other polymers.

They state that the quantitative separation of plasticizers from the other ingredients is the first and most important step in the analysis of plasticized polyvinyl chloride compositions. The most effective and convenient method of separation is by extraction with a suitable solvent, using the Soxhlet apparatus. The efficacy of this procedure depends mainly on the choice of solvent. The ideal solvent would not dissolve any of the polyvinyl chloride, but would remove all the plasticizer, and all, or none, of the other ingredients of the composition.

Haslam and Soppet[73] found that extraction with acetone, followed by precipitation of dissolved polymer with light petroleum, gave poor results: only 28·5% was recovered from a composition containing 31·8% tritolyl phosphate. Substitution of 1,2-dichlorethane for acetone gave no improvement, but diethyl ether extracted 31·8% of the sample, and the extract contained a negligible amount of polyvinyl chloride. For routine extraction it was recommended by Haslam and Soppet that the sample be stood overnight in cold ether, then extracted for 6–7 hr in the Soxhlet apparatus. This procedure had also been described by Doehring[74] who specified that anhydrous ether should be used. Thinius[75] compared the rates of extraction of dioctyl phthalate by ether, carbon tetrachloride and petroleum at room temperature. In 70 min the ether extract from a composition containing 40·0% plasticizer amounted to 39·7%; in the same time the carbon tetrachloride extract was 33·1% and the petroleum extract 29·0%. Extraction with carbon tetrachloride for 64 hr gave only 35·6% extract. Thinius also found that mixtures of phthalate and phosphate esters could be completely removed by ether, but light petroleum gave only 65% of the expected yield. Toluene dissolved some polyvinyl chloride at room temperature, and very much more in a Soxhlet extraction.

For compositions containing polypropylene adipate, which is only partly extracted by ether, Haslam and Squirrell[76] used a 6-hr ether extraction, followed by an 18-hr methanol extraction. The ether extract was 34·5% from a composition containing 36·1% of a mixture of equal parts of dioctyl phthalate and tritolyl phosphate, but only 33·1% from a composition containing 45·7% of a mixture of equal parts of dioctyl phthalate, tritolyl phosphate and polypropylene adipate. The combined ether and methanol extracts amounted to 34·7% and 44·3% respectively. Wake[77] quotes the results of some unpublished work carried out at the laboratories of the Rubber and Plastics Research Association: methanol extracted 40·5% and 36·8% from compositions containing 42·3% polypropylene sebacate and 36·4% polypropylene adipate respectively. The extracts contained polyvinyl choride equivalent to 0·6% and 0·9% respectively. Clarke and Bazill[78] extract with ether for 15 hr, then with methanol for 8 hr. They state that ether removes plasticizers whose molecular weight is less than 1000.

Robertson and Rowley[72] compared the efficacies of ether, carbon tetrachloride and methanol in the Soxhlet extraction of a number of polyvinyl chloride compositions Binary azeotropes of methanol with carbon tetrachloride, chloroform, 1,2-dichlorethane and acetone, and of diethyl ether with 1,2-epoxypropane, were also compared, and are discussed below. They also studied the effects of varying extraction times and initial plasticizer concentrations.

The polyvinyl chloride compositions were prepared by mixing the weighed ingredients by hand, then blending on a hot two-roll open mill. They were removed from the mill as

0·05 cm sheets. Each sheet of plasticized polyvinyl chloride was cut into pieces 1 cm × 0·3 cm. In every extraction the weight of sample was 2 g, and the volume of solvent 50 ml. An all-glass jacketed Soxhlet apparatus was used with Whatman 19 mm × 90 mm extraction thimbles. When each extraction was completed the solvent was distilled off, and the last traces removed by heating in the water bath for 1 hr and in the oven at 105°C for 3 hr. After cooling in air, the flask and extract were weighed, then heated in the oven for a further 30 min, cooled and reweighed. If the weights agreed to within 2 mg the first value was taken, otherwise the flask was heated for another 30 min and weighed once more.

Polymer dissolved in the extracts was detected by adding methanol to a solution of the extract in tetrahydrofuran: any polyvinyl chloride could be seen as a white precipitate.

The solvents used for the extractions were the ordinary laboratory reagent grades. Dry ether was obtained by passing the ordinary reagent (which contained about 0·3% water) through a column of activated alumina.

Extraction with Single Solvents

Table 8 shows the results obtained by extracting various compositions with ether, and with carbon tetrachloride. Carbon tetrachloride was found to be a more effective extractant than ether, but the carbon tetrachloride extracts all contained some cadmium and barium (present as stabilizers in the original PVC as barium stearate 1% and cadmium stearate 0·5%), and a trace of polyvinyl chloride. Carbon tetrachloride did not completely extract polypropylene adipate (PPA), but was satisfactory in all other cases. Ether was unsatisfactory for the extraction of both polypropylene sebacate and polypropylene adipate, and gave rather low yields of Mesamoll and TTP.

TABLE 8. EXTRACTION WITH SINGLE SOLVENTS

Plasticizer	Concn. %	Extracts, %		
		4 hr Ether	8 hr Ether	4 hr CCl₄
Bisoflex 791	28·5	28·0	28·3	29·1
Tritolyl phosphate	28·5	26·0	27·8	28·6
Mesamoll	28·5	25·2	26·7	27·9
Bisoflex 79S	28·5	28·2	28·5	29·3
Reoplex 220	28·5	20·4	23·1	28·8
Hexaplas PPA	28·5	5·4	7·1	5·8

Table 9 gives the results of a comparison of dry and water-saturated ether for the extraction of Bisoflex 791 (C_7/C_9 alcohol esters) from various compositions. No water remained in the extracts obtained by using wet ether, and these extracts gave slightly higher results than those obtained by using dried ether. There seems to be no advantage in using anhydrous ether as suggested by Doehring.[74]

Extraction with Mixed Solvents

Methanol forms minimum boiling-point azeotropes with a number of solvents which swell polyvinyl chloride, and some of these were found to be useful extractants. Table 10 gives the results of extracting PVC samples containing 28·5% Reoplex 220 with various mixtures for 4 hr. The dichlorethane/methanol and carbon tetrachloride/methanol azeotropes dissolved very little polyvinyl chloride, but appreciable quantities of it were found in the other extracts. All the extracts contained traces of cadmium and barium soaps. An azeotropic mixture of 1,2-epoxypropane and diethyl ether was tested, but this also dissolved a considerable quantity of polymer.

TABLE 9. EXTRACTION WITH DRY AND WITH WATER-
SATURATED ETHER

Plasticizer	Concn. %	Extracts, %	
		"Dry"	"Wet"
Bisoflex 791	23·5	22·1	22·7
Bisoflex 791	28·5	27·3	28·1
Bisoflex 791	33·5	32·7	33·3
Bisoflex 791	38·5	37·3	38·0

TABLE 10. EXTRACTION WITH MIXED SOLVENTS

Solvent mixture	B.p.	Extract,%
1:1, Dichlorethane/methanol	60°C	30·2
2:1, Carbon tetrachloride/methanol	56°C	30·0
4:1, Chloroform/methanol	54°C	31·8
7:1, Acetone/methanol	56°C	39·2
7:6, Ether/1,2-epoxypropane	33°C	35·7

Multiple Extractions

Table 11 gives the results of following 4 hr extractions with ether by extractions with other solvents. It can be seen that extraction for 4 hr with carbon tetrachloride/methanol azeotrope gives better results than extraction for 15 hr with methanol.

If a composition containing a polyester plasticizer and a monomeric plasticizer is extracted first with ether, then with methanol or carbon tetrachloride/methanol, the ether extract will contain nearly all the monomeric plasticizer, and some of the polyester, and the second extract will contain almost pure polyester. Table 12 gives the results of extracting a composition containing Reoplex 220 (19·0%), Bisoflex 791 (7·5%), and Bisoflex 79S (7·0%), using various procedures, and Fig. 10 shows the infrared spectra of the extracts and the original plasticizers.

Effects of Extraction Time and Plasticizer Concentration

The extraction of plasticizers from polyvinyl chloride compositions must involve diffusion processes, and the rate of extraction should depend, to some extent, on the initial plasticizer concentration. This was found to be true for the extraction of Mesamoll by ether. Compositions made from I.C.I. Corvic D65/1, lead stearate (0·1%), and Mesamoll (10–50%) were extracted with ether for 1–8 hr, and the plasticizer contents m (% w/w), at times t (hours), were calculated from the weights of the extracts. Figure 11 shows the curves obtained by plotting log (m/m_0) against t, for different values of m_0, the initial plasticizer content. In every case, except when $m_0 = 10\%$, there is initially a very rapid loss of plasticizer, followed by a period when m/m_0 decreases exponentially. When $m_0 = 10\%$, the rate of decrease of m/m_0 is very small at all stages of the extraction.

Becker[79] has given approximate solutions of the diffusion equation

$$dc/dt = \text{div} (D \text{ grad } c)$$

appropriate to diffusion out of isotropic solids of arbitrary shape when D is constant. In this case the diffusion equation reduces to

$$dc/dt = DV^2c,$$

and the proportion of the diffusing substance remaining in the solid after time t is given by

$$\frac{c - c_s}{c_0 - c_s} = \frac{\alpha}{\beta^2} \exp \left[-\beta^2 (S/V)^2 Dt \right] \tag{1}$$

where c_0 is the concentration in the solid at $t = 0$, c_s is the surface concentration at $t > 0$, c is the average concentration in the solid at $t > 0$, α and β are shape constants, and S/V is the surface-to-volume ratio. Becker[79] discusses the limits of validity of this equation, and shows that it is applicable in all cases if $(S/V^2)Dt$ is greater than 0·6. The samples used in the extraction experiments, performed by Robertson and Rowley,[72] had a surface-to-volume ratio of about 50 cm⁻¹, so that for $t > 1$ hr and $D > 10^{-7}$ cm²/sec, equation (1) should be applicable to their results, if D is constant.

TABLE 11. MULTIPLE EXTRACTIONS

Plasticizer	Concn. %	Extracts, %	
		4 hr ether, 5 hr MeOH	4 hr ether, 4 hr CCl₄ MeOH
Bisoflex 791	28·5	27·7	28·7
Tritolyl phosphate	28·5	25·8	28·9
Mesamoll	28·5	25·5	28·1
Bisoflex 79S	28·5	28·1	29·0
Reoplex 220	28·5	20·4	29·3
Hexaplas PPA	23·5	11·0	17·4

TABLE 12. EXTRACTION OF MIXED PLASTICIZERS

Solvent	Time, hr	Extract, %	
Diethyl ether	8	28·6	
Carbon tetrachloride	4	33·4	
Diethyl ether	4	27·3	
Methanol	15	0·5	27·8
Diethyl ether	4	27·2	
Carbon tetrachloride/methanol	4	6·0	33·2

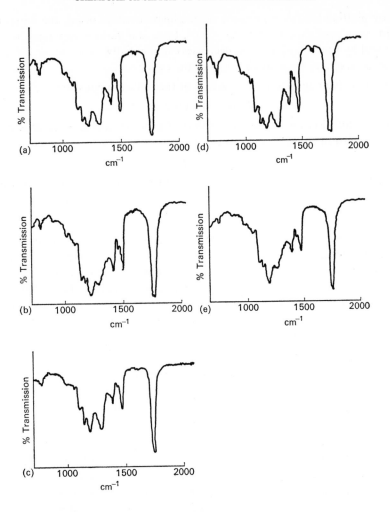

FIG. 10. Infrared spectra of PVC plasticizers and extracts.[72] (a) Mixture of Reoplex 220 (56·7%), Bisoflex 791 (22·4%). (b) Reoplex 220. (c) Carbon tetrachloride extract. (d) Ether extract. (e) Carbon tetrachloride/methanol extract.

Assuming that $c_s = 0$, S/V is constant, and $m/m_0 = c/c_0$ (none of these assumptions can be exactly true at all stages of the extraction, but should be nearly correct during the later stages), equation (1) can be written

$$\log (m/m_0) = A - \beta t \tag{2}$$

where β is proportional to $(S/V^2)Dt$. It can be seen that after the first few hours the curves are of the form given in equation (2), which can therefore be assumed to describe adequately the important later stages of the extraction process. In the earlier stages the departures from linearity are probably due to the rapidity with which D decreases as m decreases.

Improvement of Extractions

The aim in the separation of plasticizers from polyvinyl chloride compositions is to remove all the plasticizer, but in practice it is satisfactory if m is reduced to about 0·5%. The results obtained by Robertson and Rowley[72] and by other workers show that the residual plasticizer content after extraction with ether is frequently very much more than 0·5%. Extractions could be improved by increasing t, $(S/V)^2$, or D.

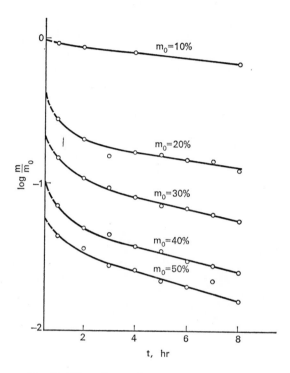

Fig. 11. Effect of extraction time (t) and plasticizer concentration (m_0) on ether extraction of Mesamoll from PVC.[72]

Increasing t is useful only if $(S/V)^2D$ is reasonably large, or m is reduced to a low value in the early stages of the extraction. This can be seen if the curves of Fig. 11 are extrapolated to values of m/m_0 equivalent to $m = 0·5\%$. For $m_0 = 50\%$ the time required to reduce m to 0·5% is about 12 hr; for $m_0 = 40\%$, 15 hr; for $m_0 = 30\%$, 24 hr; for $m_0 = 20\%$, 36 hr; for $m_0 = 10\%$, several days (it was found experimentally that after 64 hr m was 4·8%).

The surface-to-volume ratio should have a considerable effect on the rate of extraction, and the sample being extracted should always be reduced to as fine a state of sub-division as possible. Doehring[74] cut his samples in strips, cooled them so that they became rigid, and ground them up in a pencil sharpener. This method could be used for compositions plasticized with tritolyl phosphate, but is not suitable for the type of composition likely to be encountered nowadays. Samples received in sheet form are usually just cut into strips, and S/V will depend mainly on the thickness of the sheet, but wherever possible the material should be grated, using one of the tools now available. For sheet material cut into strips with scissors S/V will generally be less than 200 cm⁻¹, and may be as little as 20 cm⁻¹, but for rasped material S/V should be at least 200 cm⁻¹.

The diffusion coefficient can be increased by increasing the temperature at which extraction takes place, or by using a solvent which swells the sample more than it is swollen by diethyl ether. The first method is not practicable, but the second has been shown to be effective. The main difficulty is in finding a solvent which swells, but does not dissolve, polyvinyl chloride; the use of a constant boiling mixture of carbon tetrachloride and methanol seems to be a solution of this difficulty. Robertson and Rowley[72] have used this mixture for the extraction of residual plasticizer from a great number of commercial polyvinyl chloride compositions, after first extracting for 8 hr with ether. The only difficulties encountered were with compositions containing blends of butadiene/acrylonitrile copolymer and low molecular weight polyvinyl chloride, and by those containing vinyl chloride/vinyl acetate copolymer: the carbon tetrachloride/methanol mixture extracts appreciable amounts of polymer from such compositions.

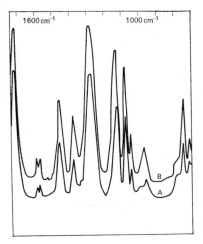

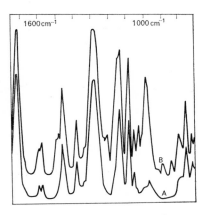

FIG. 12. Infrared spectra for (A) di-n-octyl phthalate and (B) bis-2-ethylhexyl phthalate.[80]

FIG. 13. Infrared spectra of (A) dioctyl phthalate and (B) dioctyl phthalate with an added 10% tricresyl phosphate.[80]

Two general methods of plasticizer determination were distinguished between by Guichon and Henniker:[80] with and without preliminary extraction. Either may precede infrared spectrometry or gas-phase chromatography. The most common method is to use ether to extract the plasticizers to be determined. If a quantitative analysis is required, the sample should be thin (0·1 mm or less) and should be extracted for several hours (usually 10 hr) to ensure that extraction is complete. If extraction is to be followed by spectrometry, care must be taken to eliminate all solvent by drying for 2–3 hr at 80°C. If the analysis is to be done by chromatography, drying is unnecessary since the solvent is much more volatile than the plasticizer and will be well separated.

The spectrum reveals immediately the chemical type of a single plasticizer or of the principal one if there are several. Comparison with authentic spectra often leads to the unequivocal identification of the principal plasticizer if its spectrum is available in a collection, and under good conditions homologous or isomeric plasticizers may be distinguished.

for example, di-n-octyl and bis-2-ethylhexyl phthalates. The chemical type of secondary plasticizers (phthalates, phosphates, esters of di-acids, etc.) may be established with a degree of certainty depending on the analyst's experience and the presence of absorption peaks that do not interfere with other substances extracted from the original polymer. The spectra of di-n-octyl and bis-2-ethylhexyl phthalates are compared in Fig. 12. It is evident that the difference in the region from 1000 cm^{-1} to 900 cm^{-1} which is used to distinguish these substances would be easily masked by the presence of an impurity absorbing at these frequencies. The spectrum of dioctyl phthalate containing 10% of tricresyl phosphate is added for comparison (Fig. 13). The impossibility of distinguishing phthalates in the presence of this phosphate is evident. Nevertheless, knowing the nature of the principal plasticizer, a determination of the phosphate by means of its peak at 990 cm^{-1} could be undertaken.

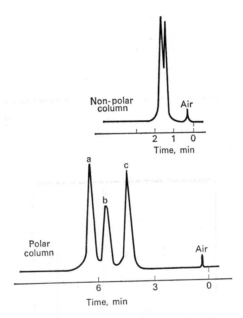

FIG. 14. Gas chromatograms showing the poor resolution of three plasticizers. (*a*) di-ethyl phthalate, (*b*) dimethyl sebacate and (*c*) tributyl phosphate—on a non-polar column; and the good separation of these substances on a polar column.

The same extraction technique may be followed by gas-phase chromatography on a special, sufficiently rapid, column. A single plasticizer is identified by its retention data with, however, an uncertainty which may be practically eliminated by the use of a chromatogram obtained on a column of different polarity. Figure 14 shows on the one hand the poor resolution of three plasticizers: (a) di-ethyl phthalate, (b) dimethyl sebacate and (c) tributyl phosphate on a non-polar column; and on the other hand, the good separation of these substances on a polar column. The two chromatograms are recorded in a period of ½–1 hr, depending on the nature of the plasticizer, the spectogram being obtained in 10 min. These times are negligible compared to the time of extraction.

Gas-phase chromatography has the advantage of providing the identification, with practically equal ease, of secondary plasticizers with a concentration of possibly only 1%

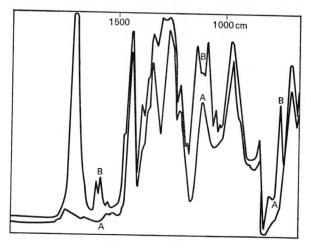

FIG. 15. Comparison of infrared spectra of pure PVC and PVC plasticized with 5% dibutyl phthalate.[80]

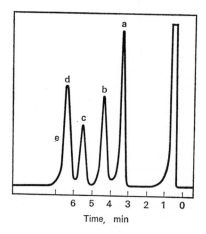

FIG. 16. Chromatogram showing separation of (a) dibutyl succinate, (b) tributyl phosphate, (c) dimethyl sebacate and (d) di-ethyl phthalate. (1) pyrolysis products of PVC.[80]

of that of the principal plasticizer. At the same time traces of acid esters or heavy alcohols may easily be detected in commercial plasticizers, as well as symmetrical esters that are usually found in unsymmetric plasticizers.

The direct analysis of plasticizers in a polymer is of considerable interest as it would eliminate the preliminary extraction. Effectively this is possible by infrared spectrometry in certain favourable cases in which one can establish the chemical type of the main plasticizer, but to draw the maximum of information from spectrometry it would be necessary to apply differential spectrometry techniques or electrical analysis of spectrograms. Figure 15 compares the spectra of pure polyvinyl chloride and PVC plasticized with 5% dibutyl phthalate. The presence of a phthalate can be detected or, if its identity is known, its concentration determined by means of the peak at 1725 cm^{-1}.

On the other hand, gas-phase chromatography, because of the physical separation it effects, furnishes both a qualitative and a quantitative analysis of polymer–plasticizer mixtures with almost the same ease as the analysis of plasticizers alone. It suffices to submit the sample, prepared as for the pyrolysis of plastics, to a controlled pyrolysis in order to disengage the vaporized plasticizers. The polymer is partially degraded, but its pyrolysis products were in all the cases studied by Guichon and Henniker[80] much lighter than the plasticizers and in no way prevented their separation and identification. Figure 16 shows the separation thus obtained of four plasticizers: (a) dibutyl succinate, (b) tributyl phosphate, (c) dimethyl sebacate and (d) di-ethyl phthalate and the pyrolysis products of polyvinyl chloride. The latter are elutriated during the first minute of operation.

The quantitative analysis of most of these plasticizers is possible with a relative standard deviation of 5%. The technique can be extended to many cases, though this needs care because of the possible thermal degradation of plasticizers not yet studied and requires an examination of each particular case. It is also always possible for plasticizers to remain in the analysis sample or fail to be elutriated from the column and escape detection. For example tricresyl phosphates and heavier products, mainly the so-called non-migrating plasticizers (polyesters, polyacrylonitrile), are quite unsuitable for determination by gas-phase chromatography. Non-migrating plasticizers, which find increasing use in industry, also present a problem in infrared spectrometry. They cannot be extracted by solvent and must thus be regarded as polymer mixtures with all their difficulties.

Criddle[81] has described a procedure for the identification and semi-quantitative determination of plasticizers based on ether extraction of the polymer followed by liquid chromatography on a Celite[454]–silica gel column (both 100–200 mesh) and, finally, by the weighing of fractions and infrared spectroscopy (discussed further in Chapter 3, Section 1). Infrared spectra of various plasticizers reported by Criddle are shown in Fig. 17.

1.7   Determination of Ultraviolet Absorbers

Among the numerous additives commonly used in plastic materials, the ultraviolet absorbers are increasing in importance because they are often used in food packaging materials to protect the plastic material as well as the foodstuff packaged from the actinic action of ultraviolet radiation. Actinic effects may cause discoloration of both the plastic material and the foodstuff, and may occasion also changes in taste and loss of vitamins in the food.

The ultraviolet absorbers can be divided in different groups:

(a) Benzophenone derivatives.
(b) Salicylic acid esters.
(c) Resorcinol esters.
(d) Benzotriazole compounds.
(e) Coumarine derivatives.

Fig. 17. Infrared spectra of plasticizers.[81]

A. Infrared spectrum of Cereclor, an ICI chlorinated hydrocarbon plastizicer.

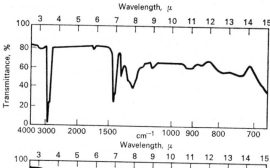

B. Spectrum of Mesamoll, a J. M. Steel & Co. Ltd. monomeric plasticizer.

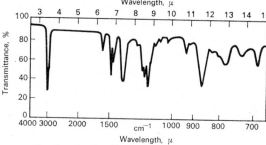

C. Spectrum of tritolyl phosphate plasticizer.

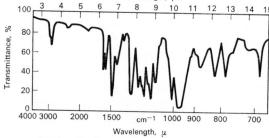

D. Spectrum of di-n-butyl phthalate.

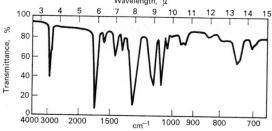

FIG. 17 (*cont.*)

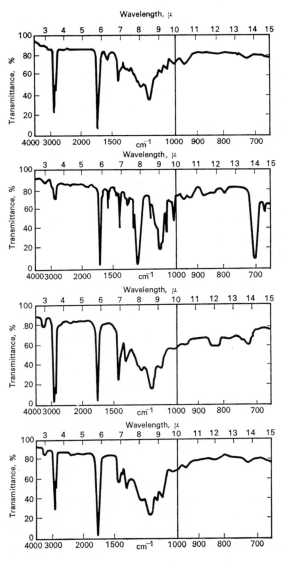

E. Infrared spectrum of di-n-butyl sebacate.

F. Diethylene glycol dibenzoate spectrum.

G. Spectrum of Abrac "A", an epoxide vegetable oil plasticizer produced by A. Boake, Roberts & Co. Ltd.

H. Polypropylene sebacate infrared spectrum.

By their nature, many of these types of compounds are amenable to analysis by fluorimetric analysis, thus Uvitex OB has an intense ultraviolet absorption at a wavelength of 378 mμ, which is high enough to be outside the region where many potentially interfering substances present in the polymer extract would be excited to fluoresce. This is illustrated in the following fluorimetric procedure for the determination of down to 10 ppm Uvitex OB in polystyrene. Antioxidants such as Ionol CP (2,6-di-tert-butyl-*p*-cresol), Ionox 330 (1,3,5-tri-methyl-2,4,6-tri(3,5-di-t-butyl-4-hydroxybenzyl)benzene), Polygard (tris(nonylated phenyl)phosphite), Wingstay T (described as a butylated cresol), and Wingstay W and many others, do not interfere in this procedure.

TABLE 13. SOME ULTRAVIOLET ABSORBERS FOR USE IN PLASTIC MATERIALS

Chemical formula	Trade name	Manufacturer
1. 2-hydroxy-4-methoxy-benzophenone	Uvinul M 40 Uvistat 24 Cyasorb UV 9	General Aniline Co. Ward & Blenkinsop Cyanamid
2. 2,4-dihydroxy-benzophenone	Uvistat 12 Uvinul 400	Ward & Blenkinsop General Aniline Co.
3. 2-hydroxy-4-methoxy-4'-methyl benzophenone	Uvistat 2211	Ward & Blenkinsop
4. 2,4,5-trihydroxy butyrophenone	Inhibitor THBP	Eastman
5. 4-dodecyloxy-2-hydroxy benzophenone	Inhibitor DOBP	Eastman
6. 2-hydroxy-4-n-octoxybenzophenone	Cyasorb UV531	Cyanamid
7. 2,2'dihydroxy-4-methoxy benzephenone	Cyasorb UV 24	Cyanamid
8. 2,2'dihydroxy-4,4'-dimethoxy benzophenone	Uvinul D 49	General Aniline Co.
9. *p*-tert-butylphenylsalicilate		
10. resorcinol mono benzoate	Inhibitor RMB	Eastman
11. hydroxyphenylbenzo-triazole	Tinuvin P	Geigy
12. 7-diethylamino-4-methyl coumarin		Ward & Blenkinsop

Method Summary

0·2 g of the polystyrene sample is shaken with chloroform to achieve solution. The sample is excited by ultraviolet radiation of wavelength 370 mμ from a mercury vapour lamp and the fluorescence spectrum of the sample recorded over the range 400–440 mμ. The reading from the fluorimeter is noted and the Uvitex OB concentration in the polystyrene determined by reference to a prepared calibration graph.

Apparatus

Spectrometer with fluorimetric attachment. Any spectrofluorimeter could be used for the determination. The procedure described below refers specifically to the Optica CF4NR spectrofluorimeter

1 cm silica fluorimetric cells

25 ml and 100 ml graduated flasks
Ultraviolet lamp (wavelength 350 mμ).
Chance OXI optical filter.
5 ml and 1 ml graduated pipettes.
Mechanical shaker.

Reagents

Chloroform; Spectroscopic or Analar grades are suitable.
Sample of polystyrene free of Uvitex OB.
Uvitex OB standard solution made by dissolving 0·0100 g of Uvitex OB in 100 ml of chloroform.

CALIBRATION. Into each of seven 100 ml volumetric flasks weigh 0·800 g of additive free polystyrene then make additions of Uvitex OB standard solution as indicated below.

Standard no.	Chloroform (ml)	Uvitex OB standard solution (ml)	ppm Uvitex in standard	ppm Uvitex in polymer
1	100 ml	Nil	Nil	Nil
2	95	5	5·0	625
3	98	2	2·0	250
4	99	1	1·0	125
5	99·5	0·5	0·5	62·5
6	99·8	0·2	0·2	25·0
7	99·9	0·1	0·1	12·5

SETTING UP THE FLUORIMETER. Mount the mercury vapour source on the Optica CF4NR and connect as described in the manufacturer's manual. Set the controls of the instrument as follows:
Console controls:

Double beam mains control	ON
Fluorimeter mains control	ON
Mode switch	SB
% switch	100%
Time constant	Normal
Gain control	5

Dynode supply:

Control button	3

Filter:

Mount Chance OXI filter between mercury vapour source and sample compartment.

Recorder:

Set to read % transmission.

Record the fluorescence spectrum of each solution, prepared as above from 400 to 440 mμ at a suitable slit width. If the 435 mμ peak is less than 15 divisions, or greater than 80 divisions in height, re-run the trace on a higher or lower slit width, respectively.

Wash out the fluorimeter cell thoroughly with chloroform and check that the final washings show no fluorescence at 435 mμ before re-filling the cell with the next solution.

Repeat the above procedure on the various solutions at various slit width settings.

Measure the height of the peaks at 435 mμ for the set of calibration solutions at each slit width setting used.

Plot a calibration curve of peak height versus the corresponding concentrations of Uvitex OB in the standard solutions.

The fluorimeter must be recalibrated whenever the mercury lamp is changed.

Analysis of Polystyrene

Fill the fluorimeter cell with standard No. 1 (see table) (i.e. chloroform and polystyrene blank) and place the cell in the fluorimeter beam.

Switch on the rotating mirrors, set the monochromator to 400 mμ and, with the recorder chart running, set the pen on zero by means of the "set zero" control.

Set the monochromator to 435 mμ. Fill the fluorimeter cell with a 1·0 ppm Uvitex standard (Standard No. 4; see table). Set slit width to a suitable value and adjust 100% control until the recorder pen gives the same reading as in the current calibration curve.

Weigh accurately 0·2 g of polymer into a 25-ml volumetric flask, add 15 ml chloroform and shake until dissolved, make up to volume with more chloroform. This solution is now ready for analysis.

Calculations

Determine the concentration (C ppm) of Uvitex OB in the solution examined by reference to the peak height vs. Uvitex concentration graph.

Calculate the concentration of Uvitex in the polymer as follows:

$$ppm \; Uvitex \; OB \; polystyrene = C \times 125 \; ppm.$$

1.8 Determination of Polygard (Tris(nonylated phenyl)-phosphite) in Styrene-Butadiene Rubbers and Latexes

The widely used method for the determination of this stabilizer is based on the determination of phosphorus. This involves a tedious preliminary digestion with nitric and perchloric acids. Nawakowski[83] has described a colorimetric method for determining Polygard based on hydrolysis to nonyl phenol, followed by coupling with *p*-nitrobenzene-diazonium fluoroborate and colorimetric estimation at 550 mμ.

Various other phenolic antioxidants produced dyes under these conditions, viz. Wingstay S, Agerite Superlite and Nevastain A.

The procedure was applied with good precision (Table 14) to the determination of Polygard in dry rubber and latexes. Good agreement was obtained between this procedure and direct determinations of phosphorus by elemental analysis (Table 15).

TABLE 14. PRECISION OF COLORIMETRIC p-NITROBENZENE DIAZONIUM FLUOROBORATE METHOD FOR DETERMINATION OF POLYGARD

Type of rubber	Polygard found, %			Av., %	Std. dev., %
Naugapol 1018 dry rubber	1·40,	1·44,	1·43	1·44	0·017
	1·46,	1·44,	1·45		
Naugapol 1504 dry rubber	1·43,	1·45,	1·45	1·43	0·025
	1·39,	1·42			
Synpol 1708 latex	0·222,	0·219,	0·210	0·217	0·011
	0·232,	0·216,	0·208		
	0·216,	0·224,	0·216		
	0·196,	0·232,	0·196		
	0·216,	0·230,	0·210		
			0·225		
Naugapol 1504 latex	0·330,	0·325		0·329	0·013
	0·335,	0·331			
		0·324			
Naugapol 1019 latex	0·338,	0·334,	0·327	0·333	0·008

TABLE 15. COMPARISON OF PHOSPHORUS AND COLORIMETRIC p-NITROBENZENE DIAZONIUM FLUOROBORATE METHODS ON POLYGARD ANALYSIS

Type of polymer	Method of analysis	Polygard found, %			Av., %	Recovery Av., %	Std. dev., %
Naugapol 1503	Colorimetric	1·22,	1·17,	1·18	1·19	101	0·027
	Phosphorus	1·17,	1·16		1·17	99	
Naugapol 1018	Colorimetric	1·20,	1·24,	1·23	1·22	98	0·021
	Phosphorus	1·23,	1·24		1·22	98	

Standard deviation by phosphorus method is 0·015%.

Brandt[84] has described an alternate method for the determination of Polygard in SBR which utilizes the bathochromic shift in the spectrum of phenols resulting from the formation of phenolate ions in alkaline solution.

Polygard in iso-octane has an ultraviolet spectrum with a peak at 273 mμ in neutral solution. By adding a strong base (tetrabutylammonium hydroxide) the Polygard is hydrolysed and the peak is shifted to 296 mμ. The difference in absorbance at 299 mμ between the neutral and alkaline solutions is directly proportional to the amount of Polygard present. By use of this bathochromic shift, interference of nonphenolic impurities is eliminated and a background correction factor is not required.

The latex is flocculated by addition of acid. Polygard is extracted by agitation and boiling with iso-octane. Excess acid, water, and carbon disulphide resulting from the decomposition of dithiocarbamates are distilled over. A portion of the extract is made alkaline and the absorbance of the alkaline solution is determined using the neutral extract as reference.

The method is accurate, simple, rapid (elapsed time less than 1·5 hr for polymer, less than 2·0 hr for latex), specific for phenolic compounds, and insensitive to interference except xanthates. Results are repeatable and agree well with those obtained with the perchloric acid method (Table 16). The method is unsatisfactory for oil-extended stock or mixtures of Polygard with other phenolic-type antioxidants.

TABLE 16. DETERMINATION OF POLYGARD. COMPARISON
OF ULTRAVIOLET WITH PERCHLORIC ACID METHODS

SBR latex Type 6101	% Polygard Perchloric Acid (phosphorus)		Ultraviolet	
Sample 1	1·31	1·30	1·18	1·30
Sample 2	1·26	1·28	1·24	1·36
Sample 3	1·23	1·24	1·36	1·32
Sheet rubber Type 1019	1·25	1·28	1·04	1·06
Type 1503	1·62	1·63	1·53	1·60
Type 1018	1·59	1·56	1·57	1·58
Type 1022	1·27	1·31	1·16	1·14

Parks *et al.*[330] have described qualitative colorimetric tests for various antioxidants in crude styrene–butadiene synthetic rubbers. The tests, which are carried out on acetone extracts of the rubber, are outlined in Tables 17 and 18. It is seen (Table 17) that Polygard can be distinguished from the other antioxidants by the reaction with Millon's reagent.

1.9   Determination of Organic Peroxides

Organic peroxides can occur in small amounts in some types of polymers such as polystyrenes as a result of the fact that a peroxide has been used as a polymerization catalyst in polymer manufacture. Also, stable organic peroxides such as dicumyl peroxide have been used as synergists, in conjunction with bromine and or phosphorus-containing additives, to impart fire resistance to cellular expanded polystyrene and other types of plastics.

Kuta and Quackenbush[85] have studied the polarography of twenty-three commercially available organic peroxides. Polagrams were recorded, using a Sargent Model XXI polarograph on solutions of these compounds in an electrolyte consisting of 0·3 M lithium chloride dissolved in 1:1 benzene:methanol, using ethylcellulose as a maximum suppressor. Half-wave potentials for some of the peroxides they examined are shown in Table 19.

The compounds fell into six different groups, based on their structures and behaviour in the polarographic cell. The first group of eight compounds, shown in Table 19, had reduction waves at or near zero voltage. Included were diaroyl and diacyl peroxides and peroxy acids. The diaroyl peroxides (benzoyl and bis(2,4-dichlorobenzoyl) peroxides) showed linear relationships between diffusion current and concentration in the range 9×10^{-2} to 4×10^{-4} M, and the diacyl peroxides (acetyl, lauroyl, and succinic acid peroxides) between 1×10^{-2} and 1×10^{-4} M. The succinic acid peroxide showed a second reduction

TABLE 17. COLOUR REACTIONS OF INDIVIDUAL ANTIOXIDANTS IN THE ACETONE-EXTRACTABLE PORTION OF SBR[1]

Reagent	PBNA[2]	BLE[3]	Stalite[4]	Wingstay S[5]	Polygard[6]	Blank
Iodine monochloride	Red-purple with a ppt	Blue-purple with a ppt	Red-purple	Pink	Pink	Yellow
Sodium hydroxide dissolved in ethanol added to product of ICl reaction	Yellow-green or brown-green	Brilliant blue	Yellow-green	Bright yellow	Colourless	Colourless
Liebermann's	Brown	Deep blue-green	Light blue-green	Pink	Yellow	Colourless
Ceric nitrate	Light brown	Red-brown	Green	Orange	Green-yellow	Yellow
Millon's	Orange	Brown	Orange	Slowly yellow	Slowly red	Colourless
Aqueous p-nitro-benzene-diazonium chloride	Purple or red	Light Brown	Yellow, rapidly changing to red	Yellow	Yellow	Yellow
Alcoholic p-nitro-benzene-diazonium chloride	Red	Very light brown	Yellow, slowly changing to red	Yellow	Yellow	Yellow
Benzoyl peroxide	Faint purple soln. and purple outer ring in 2–3 min	Faint purple soln. and purple ring in 30–60 sec	Pale gray soln. and gray ring in 3–5 min	Colourless	Colourless	Colourless
Mixture of conc. sulphuric and conc. nitric acid	Brown	Deep green	Light green	Yellow	Yellow	Colourless
5-nitroso-8-quinolinol	Orange	Blue-green	Orange	Orange	Orange	Orange
Alpha-nitroso-beta-naphthol	Brown	Blue-green	Brown	Brown	Brown	Brown
Nitroso R salt	Yellow	Green	Yellow	Yellow	Yellow	Yellow

[1] Antioxidant concentration in the SBR was approximately 1·25%.
[2] PBNA (phenyl-beta-naphthylamine, N-phenyl-2-naphthylamine).
[3] BLE (high-temperature reaction product of diphenylamine and acetone, trade name of Naugatuck Chemical Div., U.S. Rubber Co.).
[4] Stalite (mixture of heptylated and octylated diphenylamines, trade name of B. F. Goodrich Chemical Co.).
[5] Wingstay S (mixture of styrenated phenols, trade name of Goodyear Tyre and Rubber Co.).
[6] Polygard (mixture of alkylated arylphosphites, trade name of Naugatuck Chemical Div., U.S. Rubber Co.).

CHEMICAL ANALYSIS OF ADDITIVES IN PLASTICS

TABLE 18. DETECTION OF STAINING ANTIOXIDANTS IN THE PRESENCE OF NONSTAINING ANTIOXIDANTS IN THE ACETONE EXTRACTABLE PORTION OF SBR[1,2]

Reagents Antioxidants	Iodine monochloride	Millon's reagent	Aqueous p-nitro-benzene-diazonium chloride	Alcoholic p-nitro-benzene-diazonium chloride	Nitroso R salt in conc. sulphuric acid
PBNA-Stalite	Purple, then rust red: flocculent ppt (100)	—	—	Red sol'n (50)	—
BLE-Stalite	Purple, then rust red: flocculent ppt (100)	—	—	—	—
Stalite	Purple, then rust red: no ppt	—	—	Yellow or light orange sol'n	—
PBNA-Wingstay S	Pink, does not change (100)	Amber sol'n: slight white ppt (100)	Orange sol'n: violet ring (50)	—	—
BLE-Wingstay S	Pink, changing slowly to purple (100)	Amber sol'n: slight white ppt (100)	—	—	Green ppt (10)
Wingstay S	Pink, changing slowly to orange	Yellow sol'n: slight white ppt	Yellow sol'n: changing to orange	—	Orange-green ppt
PBNA-Polygard	Pink, does not change (100)	Amber sol'n: heavy white ppt (100)	Orange sol'n: violet ring (10)	—	—
BLE-Polygard	Pink, changing slowly to purple (100)	Amber sol'n: heavy white ppt (100)	—	—	Green ppt (50)
Polygard	Pink, changing slowly to orange	Yellow sol'n: heavy white ppt	Yellow sol'n: changing to orange	—	Yellow-green ppt

[1] The figures in parentheses indicate the limits of detection of staining antioxidant (PBNA or BLE) in parts per million in SBR in the presence of about 1·25% of the nonstaining antioxidant. The colours given are for these limiting concentrations.

[2] Colours or precipitates are listed only for the useful reactions.

wave, at -1.44 V, which was attributed to the free acid group; a polarogram of succinic acid showed a reduction wave at approximately the same potentials.

Peroxyacetic and peroxybenzoic acids gave reduction waves at 0.00 voltage in the presence of ethylcellulose and methylene blue, but they did not demonstrate a linear relationship between diffusion current and concentration. The acids evidently reacted slowly with the methanol in the solvent, as a continuous decrease in diffusion current was observed with increased time of contact. Peroxyacetic acid showed an additional wave at a half-wave potential of -1.41 V, probably because of the presence of acetic acid, whose half-wave potential was observed to be 1.44 V. Bis(1-hydroxyheptyl) peroxide gave two reduction waves at 0.00 and -1.20 V. A linear relationship existed between the concentration (1×10^{-2} to 1.3×10^{-4} M) and diffusion current at half-wave potential of -1.20 V, but not at 0.00 voltage.

In the second group, in Table 19, two reduction waves were obtained for each of the three peroxides, the first at -0.60 to -0.70 V, the second at -1.05 to -1.26 V. Methyl ethyl ketone peroxide in dimethyl phthalate showed three half-wave potentials, one of which (-1.82 V) was attributed to the phthalate ester, The first reduction wave (0.60 V) was observed only when the concentration of peroxide was below 0.01 M, and the relationship between diffusion current and concentration was nonlinear, since diffusion current showed a maximum at a concentration of 2.1×10^{-3} M. The second reduction wave (half-wave potential, -1.26 V) demonstrated a linear relationship between diffusion current and the above concentrations. The samples of phenylcyclohexane hydroperoxide and di-tert-butyl perphthalate showed, for both reduction waves, a linear relationship between diffusion current and concentration in the range of 10^{-2} to 10^{-4} M.

Group three consisted of two peroxy esters (tert-butyl perbenzoate and tert-butyl peracetate) which gave a single reduction wave at about -1.0 V. Both compounds showed a linear relationship between diffusion current and concentration in the range of 10^{-2} to 10^{-4} M.

The fourth group of seven hydroperoxides also showed a single reduction wave, and at a slightly more negative potential than the third group. The group consisted of diisopropylphenyl, tert-butyl-isopropylphenyl, p-menthane, cumene, pinane, and tert-butyl hydroperoxides, and hydrogen peroxide. Five of the more complex members of the group reduced in the range of -1.02 ± 0.02 V. All gave a linear relationship between diffusion current and concentration in the range 10^{-2} to 10^{-4} M.

In a class by itself (Group 5) was the transannular peroxide ascaridole, which reduced at -1.22 V. It showed a linear relationship between diffusion current and concentration in the range 9.2×10^{-2} to 1.6×10^{-3} M.

Two peroxides, di-tert-butyl peroxide and 1-phenylmethyl-tert-butyl peroxide, were not reduced in the voltage span of 0.00 to -2.00 V.

The procedure of Kute and Quackenbush[85] can be modified to the determination in polystyrene of relatively simple organic peroxides such as benzoyl peroxide, para-tert-butyl perbenzoate and lauroyl peroxide, and would no doubt be amenable to the determination of other types of peroxides. In these procedures a suitable weight of polymer is dissolved in toluene and then an equal volume of 0.6 M lithium chloride in methanol is added. Precipitated polymer is removed by centrifuging and peroxides determined in the filtrate by cathode-ray polarography. Polymerization additives, styrene monomer or antioxidants in the polymer do not interfere in the polarographic procedure. A procedure for the determination of down to 20 ppm p-tert-butyl perbenzoate in polystyrene is given below.

TABLE 19. POLAROGRAPHIC BEHAVIOUR OF ORGANIC PEROXIDE COMPOUNDS

Compounds	Peroxide structure	Peroxide content, %	Half-wave potential, volts
GROUP 1			
Benzoyl peroxide[a]		97·9	0·00
Bis(2,4-dichloro-benzoyl)peroxide[b]		99·6	0·00
Succinic acid peroxide[b]		96·8	0·00
Lauroyl peroxide[b]		99·3	−0·15
Acetyl peroxide[c]		48·4	−0·28
Bis(1-hydroxyl-heptyl)peroxide[b]		94·2	−0·00 −1·20
Peroxyacetic acid	CH_3C-OOH	23·6	0·00
Peroxybenzoic acid		—	0·00
GROUP 2			
Methyl ethyl ketone peroxide[b]		49·3	−0·60 −1·26
Phenylcyclohexane hydroperoxide[d]		97·8	−0·66 −1·08
Di-tert-butyl per-phthalate[b]		49·8	−0·70 −1·05

TABLE 19—*continued*

Compounds	Peroxide structure	Peroxide content, %	Half-wave potential, volts
GROUP 3			
tert-Butyl per-acetate[b]	CH$_3$C(=O)—O—O—C(CH$_3$)$_3$	98·8	−1·02
tert-Butyl perbenzoate[b]	(C$_6$H$_5$)—C(=O)—O—O—C(CH$_3$)$_3$	92·6	−0·95
GROUP 4			
p-Menthane hydro-peroxide[d]	(structure)	44·1	−1·06
Cumene hydro-peroxide[d]	(structure)	96·5	−1·08
tert-Butylisopropyl-phenylhydro-peroxide[e]	(structure)	26·9	−1·06
Pinane hydro-peroxide[d]	(structure)	90·3	−1·08
Diisopropylphenyl-hydroperoxide[d]	(structure)	97·7	−1·10
tert-Butyl hydro-peroxide[b]	(CH$_3$)$_3$—C—O—O—H	56·8	−1·15
Hydrogen peroxide	H—O—O—H	22·8	−1·16
GROUP 5			
Ascaridole[f]	(structure)	—	−1·22
GROUP 6			
Di-tert-butyl peroxide[b]	(CH$_3$)$_3$—C—O—O—C(CH$_3$)$_3$	[g]	Not reduced
1-Phenylmethyl tert-butyl-per-oxide	(structure)	[g]	Not reduced

[a] Eastman Kodak Co.
[b] Lucidol Division, Wallace and Tiernan, Inc.
[c] Buffalo Electrochemical Co., Inc.
[d] Hercules Powder Co.
[e] Philips Petroleum Co.
[f] Blos Instruments Inc.
[g] No source.

Determination of p-*tert-butyl Perbenzoate in Polystyrene*

Apparatus

Cathode-ray polarograph, with dropping mercury electrode, 10 ml polarograph cells and thermostatted (25°C) water bath.

Agla micrometer syringe capable of delivery 0·01 cc with an accuracy of 0·0002 ml, available from Burroughs Wellcome and Company, London.

Volumetric glassware, pipettes 50 ml, 25 ml, 5 ml; volumetric flasks 100 ml.

Centrifuge "Super-medium", manufactured by Measuring Scientific Instruments Limited, to take 250 ml centrifuge bottles.

Reagents

Toluene, redistilled pure grade, rendered peroxide-free by shaking 1 l of the solvent with 10–20 ml of ferrous sulphate solution—prepare by mixing 60 g ferrous sulphate, 6 ml concentrated sulphuric acid and 110 ml distilled water—followed by redistillation. Store in a well-stoppered brown glass bottle.

Base electrolyte (0·6 M) remove peroxides from 1 l of methyl alcohol as described above. Weigh out 2·544 g lithium chloride (Analar) and make up to 100 ml with methyl alcohol.

Para-tert-butyl perbenzoate obtainable from British Drug Houses Limited, Poole, Dorset.

Standard addition solution. Prepare by diluting a suitable weight of *p*-tert-butyl perbenzoate with toluene.

Nitrogen white spot, oxygen content less than 25 ppm.

Mercury, pure for polarographic analysis, use trebly distilled mercury, the manufacturers should be requested to supply this mercury in stone containers. Over a period of time, mercury picks up an impurity from polyethylene storage bottles which might interfere in polarography.

Procedure

Weigh out $5·0 \pm 0·01$ g of sample and transfer to a 250-ml Pyrex glass centrifuge bottle. Measure 50 ml of toluene into the bottle. Drop a polythene coated magnetic stirrer rotor into the bottle and stopper with a cork (avoid rubber bungs). Stand the bottle on a magnetic stirrer and leave for several hours until the sample has completely dissolved or dispersed in the solvent. Accurately pipette into the gently stirred contents of the bottle 50 ml of 0·6 M lithium chloride reagent.

Insert the bottle in a centrifuge and spin at 700–900 *g* until insolubles have completely settled to the bottom of the bottle leaving an absolutely clear upper phase containing all the peroxide present in the original sample.

Dilute 50 ml toluene with 50 ml of lithium chloride solution to serve as a blank. Pipette 5 ml of the sample solution and 5 ml of the blank solution into two polarographic cells and immerse these in the constant temperature tank of the cathode-ray polarograph (thermostatted at 25°C). Carry out the degassing operations described below on the sample and on the blank solutions immediately before carrying out all polarographic measurements.

Connect a supply of oxygen-free nitrogen to the polarographic cell. Lower the dropping mercury electrode system over this cell, so that the outer glass sleeve of the electrode dips 1–2 mm into the water tank (providing a water seal to prevent the ingress of atmospheric oxygen). Immerse the anode connection in the side arm of the polarographic cell. Pass nitrogen for 15 min to completely displace oxygen from the cell solution, then switch off the nitrogen. Leave the glass sleeve in position to prevent re-entry of atmospheric oxygen into the cell solution and carry out the polarographic measurements described below within 1 to 3 min of stopping the gas purge.

The analytical conditions with the Southern Analytical Davis Differential A1660 cathode-ray polarograph (with single cell operation) are as follows:

Cathode	dropping mercury
Reference anode	mercury pool
Circuit	forward sweep (with derivative units control switch off)
Sensitivity control	select a suitable current scale-factor and keep this constant throughout the analysis. Alter the instrument sensitivity by means of the shunt scale-factor control.
Start potential	-0.7 V

By means of the "Y"-shift control, adjust the light spot to the origin of axes on the left-hand side of the graticule on the cathode-ray tube. Repeat this operation at different shunt scale-factor settings, until the polarographic wave is visible on the graticule.

The analytical conditions with the Southern Analytical K1000 polarograph are as follows:

Cathode	dropping mercury
Reference anode	mercury pool
Circuit	cathodic direct
Start potential	-0.7 V

Adjust the polarograph to its maximum sensitivity setting. Adjust the "X"-shift control and the "Y"-shift controls until the light spot commences its sweep at the origin of axes at the left-hand side of the graticule on the cathode-ray tube. Repeat this operation at different sensitivity settings until the polarographic wave is visible on the graticule.

Take the readings on the freshly degassed solutions as follows. Adjust the polarograph to the para-tert-butyl perbenzoate start potential (-0.7 V) and obtain the wave as described above for the polystyrene sample solution. Read off from the graticule the maximum height of the peak (at about -0.9 V). Raise the dropping mercury electrode from the cell and deliver as quickly as possible into the sample solution by means of a horizontally held Agla syringe a suitable "standard addition" of a toluene solution of para-tert-butyl perbenzoate (ensure that the weight of peroxide present in the "standard addition" is similar to that already present in the cell solution). Limit the volume of "standard addition" solution to less than 0.05 ml in order to avoid dilution errors. Lower the electrode into the sample cell and again pass nitrogen for 2 min. Immediately read the new peak height at -0.9 V. Similarly, determine the peak height at -0.9 V on the degassed polystyrene-free reagent blank solution.

Calculations

Para-tert-butyl perbenzoate (ppm w/w)

$$= \frac{100 \times M \times 10^6}{5 \times W} \times \left[\frac{(h_1 S_1 - h_3 S_3)}{(h_2 S_2 - h_1 S_1)} \right]$$

C

where W = weight (g) of polystyrene sample taken for analysis (assuming 5 ml portion taken for polarography),

h_1 = peak height (graticule divisions) of sample solution before standard addition,

h_2 = peak height (graticule divisions) of sample solution after standard addition,

h_3 = peak height (graticule divisions) of polymer-free reagent blank solution,

S_1, S_2 and S_3 are the corresponding instrument sensitivity settings (the product of h and S are known as peak currents in micro-amps),

M = weight (g) of para-tert-butyl perbenzoate in volume of "standard addition" solution added to cell solution.

Gas chromatography has also been used to determine certain types of organic peroxides. Bukata et al.,[86] for example, describe procedures involving chromatography of heptane solutions of peroxide (Table 20) on phthalate/diatomaceous earth or silicone/diatomaceous earth columns and using helium as the carrier gas. No doubt, this type of procedure could be easily adapted to the examination of solvent extracts of polymers.

TABLE 20. GAS CHROMATOGRAPHY. RETENTION TIMES FOR ORGANIC PEROXIDES

Compound	Column[a]	Temp., °C	Helium[b] pressure, psi	Retention time, min
tert-Butyl hydroperoxide	2 m-A	80	20	22·7
tert-Pentyl hydroperoxide	1 m-A	80	15	19·9
tert-Butyl peracetate	1 m-A	100	20	6·5
tert-Butyl peroxyisobutyrate	1 m-A	100	20	15·3
Di-tert-butyl peroxide	2 m-A	80	20	8·1
Di-tert-pentyl peroxide	1 mA	80	15	15·4
2,5-Dimethyl-2,5-di-(tert-butyl peroxy)-3-hexyne	1 m-O	138	15	4·9
2,5-Dimethyl-2,5-di(tert-butyl peroxy)hexane	1 m-O	138	15	6·9
n-Heptane	2 m-A	80	20	6·1
n-Dodecane	1 m-O	138	15	3·1
n-Pentane	1 m-A	100	20	0·4
n-Nonane	1 m-A	100	20	4·9

[a] Length (meters) and type of column used.
[b] Inlet pressure.
A, didecyl phthalate on diatomaceous earth.
O, silicon grease on diatomaceous earth.

Hyden[308] describes a gas chromatographic procedure for the determination of di-tert-butyl peroxide. This is based on the thermal decomposition of the peroxide in benzene solution into acetone and ethane when the solution is injected into the gas chromatographic column at 310°C. The technique is calibrated against standard solutions of pure di-tert-butyl peroxide of known concentration.

Certain types of peroxides used in polymer formulations are extremely stable and unreactive. This applies to substances such as dicumyl peroxide used as an ingredient of some self-extinguishing grades of polymers.

$$CH_3-\overset{\overset{\displaystyle CH_3}{|}}{\underset{|}{C}}-O-O-\overset{\overset{\displaystyle CH_3}{|}}{\underset{|}{C}}-CH_3$$

This substance cannot be determined by polarography and will not react with many of the reagents normally used for determining organic peroxides.

Brammer et al.[87] have described a method for determining dicumyl peroxide in polystyrene, which is not subject to interference by other organic peroxides or additives that may be present in the polymer. The dicumyl peroxide is extracted from the polymer with acetone and then separated from any other additives present by thin-layer chromatography on silica gel. The gel in the area of the plate containing dicumyl peroxide is then isolated and digested with potassium iodide in glacial acetic acid followed by titration of the liberated iodine by titration with very dilute sodium thiosulphate solution. This procedure has a precision of $\pm 12\%$ of the determined value with polymers containing 0·25 to 0·5% dicumyl peroxide. It is a rather time-consuming procedure but has the advantage of avoiding all risk of interference from other types of peroxides present in the sample.

1.10   Determination of Styrene, Acrylonitrile and Methacrylonitrile Monomers

Probably the best procedures available for the determination of styrene monomer in polymers are those based on gas chromatography as described in Chapter 4. Alternative methods are, however, available based on ultraviolet spectroscopy and on polarography.

Direct Ultraviolet Spectroscopic Method for Styrene

In this method,[261] the polystyrene sample (0·5 g) is dissolved in 50 ml of chloroform or another suitable spectroscopic solvent and the ultraviolet spectrum recorded in the region 280–310 mμ against polymer-free solvent in the reference cell. If the polymer is incompletely soluble in the solvent (e.g. due to the presence of gel or pigments), it is dissolved in 30 ml of solvent and the suspension filtered rapidly under light vacuum through an asbestos pad to remove insolubles.

It is essential to ensure that negligible solvent evaporation occurs during filtration. The filtrate is then made up to 50 ml and the ultraviolet spectrum recorded as already described. Calibration is performed by applying the technique to solutions prepared by including various known amounts of pure styrene monomer in 1% w/v solutions of styrene-free polystyrene.

Conventional and high impact polystyrenes contain various non-polymer additives (e.g. lubricants) which result in widely different and unknown background absorptions at the wavelength maximum at which styrene monomer is evaluated (292 mμ). The influence of the background absorptions on the evaluation of the optical density due to styrene monomer is overcome by the use of an appropriate baseline technique, claimed to make the method virtually independent of absorptions due to polymer additives. In this technique, a straight line is drawn on the recorded spectrum across the absorption peak at 292 mμ in such a way that the baseline is tangential to the absorption curve at a point close to the absorption minima occurring at 288 mμ and 295–300 mμ (Fig. 18). A vertical line is drawn from the tip of the styrene absorption peak at 292 mμ to intersect the baseline and the height of this line is then a measure of the optical density due to the true styrene monomer content of the test solution.

This baseline correction technique can obviously be applied to the determination of styrene monomer in polystyrene only if any other ultraviolet absorbing constituents in the polymer extract (e.g. lubricants, antioxidants) absorb linearly in the wavelength range 288–300 mμ. If the polymer extract contains polymer constituents other than styrene with non-linear absorptions in this region, then incorrect styrene monomer contents will be obtained. An obvious technique for removing such non-volatile ultraviolet absorbing compounds is by distillation of the extract followed by ultraviolet spectroscopic analysis of the distillate for styrene monomer (see below).

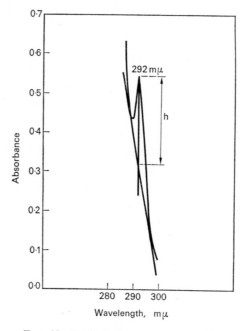

Fig. 18. Typical absorption curve of a polystyrene containing styrene monomer ultraviolet.

Distillation/Ultraviolet Spectroscopic Method for Styrene[261]

The polystyrene sample (0·5 g) is dissolved in chloroform or ethylene dichloride (20 ml) in a stoppered flask and the solution is poured into an excess of methyl alcohol (110 ml) to reprecipitate dissolved polymer. The polymer is filtered off and washed with methanol (120 ml) and the combined filtrate and washings gently distilled to provide 200 ml of distillate containing only styrene monomer and any other distillable component of the original polystyrene sample. Non-volatile polymer components (viz. stabilizers, lubricants and low molecular weight polymer) remain in the distillation residue.

The optical density of the distillate is measured either at 292 mμ or by the baseline method against the distillate obtained in a polymer-free blank distillation. Calibration is performed by applying the distillation procedure to solutions of known weights of pure styrene monomer in the appropriate quantities of methyl alcohol and the chlorinated solvent.

Table 21 shows results obtained for styrene monomer determinations carried out on two samples of pigmented polystyrene by the direct ultraviolet method and by the distillation modification of this method. It is seen that the distillation method gives results that are consistently some 0·1% higher than those obtained by direct spectroscopy, indicating that additives present in the polystyrene are interfering in the latter method of analysis.

TABLE 21. COMPARISON OF DIRECT ULTRAVIOLET AND DISTILLA-TION/ULTRAVIOLET METHODS FOR THE DETERMINATION OF STYRENE MONOMER

Method	Solvent	Styrene monomer, % w/w	
		Polystyrene sample	
		No. 1	No. 2
Direct UV method	Chloroform	< 0·05	0·13
	Carbon tetra-chloride	< 0·05	0·13, 0·14 0·16, 0·18
	Ethyl acetate	< 0·05	0·14, 0·12 0·14, 0·14 0·15
Distillation/ UV method	Ethylene di-chloride/ methanol	0·16, 0·18 0·16, 0·18 0·20	0·27, 0·29 0·26, 0·29 0·29

Both polystyrene samples contained an ester and a mineral oil type of lubricant together with a phenolic antioxidant†. The lubricants have little absorption in the 280–300 mμ region and do not interfere in either method of analysis at the 5–10% concentrations at which they are used in polystyrene formulations. The absorption spectrum of the phenolic antioxidant, however, shows a sharply decreasing non-linear absorbance in the 280–300 mμ region and contributes significantly to the background absorption of the test solution in the direct ultraviolet spectroscopic method. This invalidates the baseline correction procedure and leads to erroneous styrene monomer values. In the distillation procedure, however, the test solution used for spectroscopy does not contain the phenolic antioxidant and there is no interference in the determination of styrene monomer.

Table 22 shows the results obtained by applying the two methods discussed above to synthetic blends of pure styrene monomer in polystyrene both in the presence and in the absence of 0·5% w/w added phenolic antioxidant. The direct ultraviolet method gives correct styrene monomer contents only when the polymer does not contain the phenolic antioxidant. In its presence, determined styrene monomer contents are appreciably lower than the true values. Also, as expected, when the phenolic antioxidant is removed from the test solution by distillation, correct styrene monomer contents are obtained.

Similar effects to these were also observed with polystyrene containing other ultraviolet absorbing additives. Thus, the influence of a mixture of 0·4% w/w tris-(nonylated phenyl)

† Wingstay T, described as a butylated cresol and supplied by the Goodyear Tyre & Rubber Co.

phosphite (Polygard) and 0·2% w/w 2,6-di-tert-butyl-*p*-cresol (Ionol CP) on the determination of styrene monomer is shown in Table 22.

TABLE 22. INFLUENCE OF PHENOLIC ANTIOXIDANT[a] ON THE DETERMINATION OF STYRENE MONOMER BY DIRECT ULTRAVIOLET AND BY DISTILLATION/ULTRAVIOLET METHODS

	Styrene found, % w/w			
	Direct UV method[b]		Distillation/UV method	
Styrene added to polystyrene, % w/w	No phenolic antioxidant[a] addition	0·5% phenolic antioxidant[a] added on polymer	No phenolic antioxidant[a] addition	0·5% phenolic antioxidant[a] addition on polymer
0·11	0·11, 0·11	0·04, 0·08	0·12	0·12
0·22	0·22	0·11	—	—
0·27	0·26	0·18	0·29	0·26
0·41	0·41, 0·40	0·30, 0·27	0·40	0·40

[a] Wingstay T.
[b] Chloroform used as a sample solvent.

TABLE 23. INFLUENCE OF POLYGARD/IONOL CP MIXTURE ON DETERMINATION OF STYRENE MONOMER BY DIRECT ULTRAVIOLET AND BY DISTILLATION/ULTRAVIOLET METHODS

	Styrene found, % w/w				
	Direct UV method[a]			Distillation U/V method[a]	
Styrene added to polystyrene % w/w	No additive	0·4% w/w Polygard and 0·2% w/w Ionol CP added on polymer		No additive	0·4% w/w Polygard and 0·2% w/w Ionol CP added on polymer
0·10	0·10, 0·10	— [b]		0·11	0·11 0·09
0·26	0·25, 0·26	0·16	0·16	0·26	0·27 0·25
0·41	0·42, 0·41	0·29	0·29	0·41	0·40 0·42

[a] Chloroform used as sample solvent.
[b] Not measurable due to strong interference by additives.

Direct ultraviolet spectroscopic methods are reliable only in the case of polystyrene samples that do not contain ultraviolet absorbing antioxidants or any other type of strongly ultraviolet absorbing additive. The more lengthy distillation/ultraviolet spectroscopic method, however, will give correct results in the presence of such additives unless the additive is both sufficiently volatile to distil and absorbs in the same region of the spectrum as styrene monomer. Frequently the nature of the additives present in a polystyrene sample submitted for monomer analysis is unknown and, to overcome as far as possible any interference from this source, it is recommended that the distillation step is included in the analysis.

Polarographic Method for Acrylonitrile

Residual amounts of styrene and acrylonitrile monomers usually remain in manufactured batches of styrene–acrylonitrile copolymers. As these copolymers have a potential use in the food-packaging field, it is necessary to ensure that the content of both of these monomers in the finished copolymer is below a stipulated level.

Styrene monomer can be determined in styrene–acrylonitrile copolymers by ultraviolet spectroscopy. A satisfactory spectroscopic method has not been described, however, for determining low concentrations of acrylonitrile monomer. A published procedure[269] for determining acrylonitrile monomer involves reaction with an excess of a standard solution of dodecyl mercaptan and subsequent determination of the unreacted mercaptan by titration with standard potassium bromate–potassium iodide solution in acidic medium. However, this procedure cannot be used for determining less than 300 or 400 ppm of acrylonitrile in polymer.

Claver and Murphy have reported a polarographic method[270] for determining down to 30 ppm of residual acrylonitrile in styrene–acrylonitrile copolymers. Crompton and Buckley[271] modified this procedure, improving its sensitivity to a lower detection limit of 2 ppm acrylonitrile in polymer. They also found that it was possible, using the same base electrolyte, to determine styrene monomer in amounts down to 20 ppm in styrene–acrylonitrile copolymers. Methacrylonitrile can also be determined if acrylonitrile is absent. Both styrene and acrylonitrile can also be determined in acrylonitrile–butadiene–styrene terpolymers, using the same procedure. Tetrabutylammonium iodide (0·1 M) in aqueous dimethyl formamide was used as the base electrolyte and polarography was carried out using a Southern Instruments Davis differential cathode ray polarograph.

Figures 19 and 20 show polarograms of single solutions of acrylonitrile and styrene monomers in the base electrolyte, and of a mixture of the two monomers. It is seen that the waves for the two monomers are well resolved from each other.

The method is described below:

Apparatus

Cathode-ray polarograph—K1000 or Davis Differential Model. Complete with stand for dropping mercury electrode, polarographic cells (10 ml) and thermostatted (at 25°C) water-bath, supplied by Southern Analytical Ltd., Frimley Road, Camberley, Surrey.

Agla micrometer syringe—capable of delivering 0·01 ml with an accuracy of 0·0002 ml, available from Burroughs Wellcome and Co., London.

Calibrated glassware—pipettes, 25- and 5-ml capacities; 50-ml calibrated flasks.

Reagents

N,N'-Dimethylformamide—available from the British Drug Houses Limited, Poole, Dorset. This material is usually sufficiently pure, as supplied, for polarographic

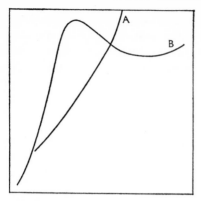

FIG. 19. Cathode-ray polarogram of a synthetic solution of acrylonitrile in tetrabutylammonium iodide-dimethylformamide base electrolyte. Curve A, base-electrolyte blank solution. Curve B, 9 ppm of a crylonitrile in base electrolyte. Start potential, −1·7 V.[271]

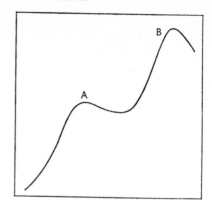

FIG. 20. Cathode-ray polarogram of a synthetic solution of 11·2 ppm of styrene and 9·3 ppm of acrylonitrile monomer in tetrabutylammonium iodide-dimethylformamide base electrolyte. Wave A, acrylonitrile wave. Wave B, styrene wave. Start potential −1·7 V.[271]

analysis. If the reagent is impure, high blank readings are obtained during polarography. The dimethylformamide blank value may be reduced by suitable purification of the reagent as described below.

First dry the solvent (1 l) by standing it over 50 g of anhydrous potassium carbonate for 3 days. Distill the product through an 80-cm Fenské column. Discard the first 200 ml of distillate and collect in a dry flask the fraction boiling between 151·5° and 153°C.

Tetrabutylammonium iodide base electrolyte, 0·2 M in dimethylformamide– pure solid is available from Kodak Limited, Kirkby, Liverpool (Code No. 4702).

Weigh 7·39 ± 0·01 g of solid anhydrous tetrabutylammonium iodide into a beaker and dissolve it in 100 ml of a dimethylformamide–water (9 + 1 v/v) mixture. (Use dimethylformamide that has been freshly purged with hydrogen or nitrogen.) Prepare this reagent freshly each day. With impure batches of tetrabutylammonium iodide a high reagent blank value is obtained in the potential range used in the polarographic analysis. In this instance purify the solid base electrolyte as described below.

Dissolve 10 g of tetrabutylammonium iodide in 100 ml of a methanol–acetone (1 + 3 v/v) mixture and filter it through paper. Leave this solution to evaporate to about half its original volume in a clean laboratory atmosphere. Add 10 ml of water to reprecipitate the salt in the form of fine crystals. Recover the crystals by filtration, dry them *in vacuo* and store them in an evacuated desiccator.

Acrylonitrile and styrene monomers—these monomers may be obtained from Kodak Limited, Kirkby, Liverpool. Store them in a refrigerator. Redistill the monomers immediately before use.

Mercury—for polarographic analysis. Use trebly distilled mercury. Request the manufacturers to supply this mercury in stone containers as it has been shown that, over a period of time, mercury picks up an impurity that might interfere in polarography from polyethylene storage bottles.

Hydrogen or nitrogen—extremely low oxygen content.

Procedure

Purge the stock bottle of dimethylformamide with oxygen-free nitrogen or hydrogen for 30 to 40 min to sweep out dissolved oxygen. Keep the bottle well stoppered and repurge each time it is opened. Use freshly purged dimethylformamide solvent throughout the analysis.

Weigh 1.25 ± 0.01 g of styrene–acrylonitrile sample into a 50-ml calibrated flask. Transfer by pipette 25 ml of anhydrous dimethylformamide to the flask, stopper the flask and swirl it to dissolve the polymer. Dilute the solution to the mark with the 0.2 M tetrabutylammonium iodide reagent and mix it well. For the blank solution, transfer by pipette 25 ml of dimethylformamide and 25 ml of the 0.2 M tetrabutyl-ammonium iodide reagent to a 50-ml calibrated flask and mix them well. Transfer by pipette 5 ml of the sample solution and 5 ml of the blank solution into two polarographic cells and immerse these in the constant temperature bath of the polarograph.

Purging of the cell with hydrogen and nitrogen must be performed immediately before any polarographic measurements are made. Lower the dropping mercury electrode system over this cell, so that the outer glass sleeve of the electrode dips 1 to 2 mm into the water tank (providing a water seal to prevent the ingress of atmospheric oxygen) and immerse the anode connection in the side arm of the polarographic cell. Pass hydrogen or nitrogen for 15 min, then switch off the gas supply. Carry out the polarographic measurements described below within 1 to 3 min of stopping the purge with gas.

The analytical conditions with the Southern Analytical K1000 polarograph are as follows:

Cathode	dropping mercury
Reference anode	mercury pool
Circuit	cathodic direct
Start potential	styrene -2.0 V
	acrylonitrile -1.7 V

Adjust the polarograph to its minimum sensitivity setting (i.e. $\times 25$). Adjust the "X"-shift and the "Y"-shift controls until the light spot commences its sweep at the origin of axes at the left-hand side of the graticule on the cathode-ray tube. Repeat this operation at decreasing sensitivity settings until the polarographic wave is visible on the graticule.

The analytical conditions with the Southern Analytical Davis Differential cathode-ray polarograph (with single-cell operation) are as follows:

Cathode	dropping mercury
Reference electrode	mercury pool
Circuit	forward sweep (with derivative units control switched off)
Sensitivity control	select a suitable current scale factor and keep this constant throughout the analysis. After the instrument sensitivity by means of the shunt scale-factor control
Start potential	styrene -2.0 V
	acrylonitrile -1.7 V

By means of the "Y"-shift control, adjust the light spot to the origin of axes on the left-hand side of the graticule on the cathode-ray tube. Repeat this operation at different shunt scale-factor settings until the polarographic wave is visible on the graticule.

Determination of Styrene

Take the readings of the freshly degassed sample solutions as indicated below.

Adjust the polarograph to the styrene start potential ($-2{\cdot}0$ V) and obtain the styrene wave as described above. Read off from the graticule the maximum height of the styrene peak and note the voltage, V_{STY}, at which this maximum polarographic reading occurs. Raise the electrode from the cell and deliver into the sample solution by means of a horizontally held Agla syringe a suitable "standard solution" of a solution of styrene in a dimethylformamide–water (95+5 v/v) mixture. Limit the volume of standard addition solution to less than 0·05 ml in order to avoid dilution errors. Lower the electrode into the sample cell and again pass hydrogen or nitrogen for 5 min. Note the new height of the styrene wave corresponding to V_{STY} volts.

Determination of Acrylonitrile

Take the readings indicated below on the same sample solution as used to determine styrene.

Adjust the polarograph to the acrylonitrile start potential ($-1{\cdot}7$ V). To determine acrylonitrile, repeat the operations described above for styrene by using a solution of acrylonitrile in a dimethylformamide–water (95+5 v/v) mixture to make the "standard solution" of acrylonitrile. Note the voltage, V_{ACN}, at which the maximum polarographic reading occurs.

Measurement of Reagent Blank Solution

Take the readings indicated below on the freshly degassed reagent blank solution.

Set the instrument at the styrene start potential. Adjust the instrument to obtain the reagent blank wave on the graticule. Measure the blank peak height corresponding to V_{STY} volts. Similarly, adjust the instrument to the acrylonitrile start potential and measure the blank peak height corresponding to V_{ACN} volts.

Acrylonitrile monomer content of copolymer, ppm =

$$\frac{50 \times 10^6 \times A_{ACN}}{5 \times W} \times \left[\frac{(h_1 S_1 - h_3 S_3)}{(h_2 S_2 - h_1 S_1)}\right]$$

Styrene monomer content of copolymer, ppm =

$$\frac{50 \times 10^6 \times A_{STY}}{5 \times W} \times \left[\frac{(h_4 S_4 - h_6 S_6)}{(h_5 S_5 - h_4 S_4)}\right]$$

where W = weight, in g, of original styrene–acrylonitrile copolymer sample made up to 50 ml in base electrolyte solution (5-ml portion used for polarography).

For acrylonitrile determinations:

h_1 = peak height, in cm, at V_{ACN} volts, of sample solution before the standard addition,

h_2 = peak height, in cm, at V_{ACN} volts, of sample solution after the standard addition,

h_3 = peak height, in cm, at V_{ACN} volts, of the polymer-free reagent blank solution,

S_1, S_2, S_3 are the corresponding instrument sensitivity settings (the product of h and S are known as peak currents, in μA) and

A_{ACN} the weight, in g, of acrylonitrile present in volume of "standard addition" solution added to the cell solution.

For styrene determinations:

h_4 = peak height, in cm, at V_{STY} volts, of sample solution before the standard addition,

h_5 = peak height, in cm, at V_{STY} volts, of sample solution after the standard addition,

h_6 = peak height, in cm, at V_{STY} volts, of the polymer-free reagent blank solution,

S_4, S_5, S_6 are the corresponding instrument sensitivity settings and

A_{STY} the weight, in g, of styrene present in volume of "standard addition" solution added to the cell solution.

CHAPTER 2

APPLICATION OF THIN-LAYER AND COLUMN CHROMATOGRAPHY TO THE SEPARATION AND DETERMINATION OF KNOWN ADDITIVES

In Chapter 1, methods were reviewed for examining additives present in polymers based on either direct spectroscopy of a cast polymer film or on solvent extraction of total additives from the polymer followed by quantitative chemical or physical analysis for various components in the extract.

Direct spectroscopy, although useful on occasions, has severe limitations concerning lack of sensitivity, possible degradation of additives or of polymer during the film forming operation at elevated temperatures and interference effects by the polymer itself or other additives present in the polymer when seeking the spectral features associated with a particular additive.

Examination of solvent extracts by various chemical or chemical methods of analysis also has its limitations. If the additive to be determined in the polymer extract is of known identity and providing that any other additives present in the polymer formulation and hence in the extract are known, then it is often possible to choose a suitable method of analysis which is both sufficiently sensitive and specific for the quantitative determination of the additive in question to be achieved. Indeed, this approach was adopted by several earlier workers who carried out ultraviolet[315-319] or infrared spectroscopy.[317, 321, 320, 322] If, on the other hand, as is often the case, a suitably specific chemical or physical method is not available for determining a known component in a mixture without interference from other additives present, then it is necessary to resort to the inclusion of a chromatographic step between the preparation of a solvent extract of the polymer and the final analytical determination. The application of thin-layer and column chromatography to the quantitative determination of known additives in mixtures is discussed in this chapter. If, as is often the case, no information is available regarding the types of additives present, then it is necessary to use combinations of chromatographic and spectroscopic techniques as discussed in Chapters 3 and 4.

Quantitative Determination of Known Additives by Thin-layer Chromatography

Numerous attempts have been made to adapt thin-layer chromatography for quantitative analysis. It is unfortunate, however, that many authors have not provided the basic data from which the accuracy of their methods can be calculated. Purdy and Truter[88] have outlined the features which are essential for a critical evaluation of this process.

Known amounts of pure reference compounds must be analysed iteratively so that the standard deviation, which when expressed as a percentage is the coefficient of variation, can be calculated. If the mean of a set of observations differs from the known value by more than three times the standard deviation, a systematic error is indicated.

To save time, it may be convenient to analyse several reference compounds simultaneously by using a standard mixture. To calculate the accuracy of the analytical process, the results must be presented in terms of the weights of each compound. Results presented as percentages of the mixture are valueless.

It is well known that the quantity of sample that can be processed by film chromatography is subject to an upper limit. The reason for the limit is that, as the weight of the sample is increased, so the area occupied by each fraction on the chromatogram increases. Ultimately, the resolution becomes unacceptable because contiguous fractions overlap. Purdy and Truter[88] have described several methods of quantifying thin-layer chromatography and these are discussed below under separate headings. Further experimental details than are given in this chapter on thin-layer chromatography will be discussed in Chapter 3, section 3.

Spectroscopic Methods

In this method a known weight of sample mixture is chromatographed on a thin-layer plate, usually coated with silica gel, by normal procedures. The test compound (or compounds) is extracted from the plate with a suitable solvent and the extract made up to a standard volume with solvent prior to spectrophotometric examination. If the compound contains a chromophore it may be determined directly; if not, before application to the plate, it must first be submitted to a chromogenic reaction if it is intended to use visible spectroscopy or, alternatively, ultraviolet spectroscopy can be used if the compound absorbs in this region of the spectrum. For spectrophotometric analysis the fractions from a single chromatoplate will provide sufficient material.

Several difficulties which are specific to the spectrophotometric method might be encountered. One of them arises from the fact that substances which absorb electromagnetic energy are invariably extracted from the absorbent material as well as the sample. The absorption spectrum of the impurity is non-specific; the intensity falls steadily as the wavelength increases, and at $400 \, m\mu$ it becomes small enough to be ignored. If the extent of interference by adsorbent impurities is small, then its effect may be cancelled out by suitable calibration procedures. By chromatographing known weights of pure reference compounds and determining the optical densities of the final solutions obtained from the plate, specific extinction coefficients may be calculated in terms of the weight of sample applied to the chromatogram. To minimize the errors introduced by extractable impurities, three refinements can be considered.

A portion of the adsorbent, equal in area to that of the sample, is removed from an unoccupied part of the chromatogram. It is processed in the standard manner and the extract is used as the blank solution in the spectrophotometer. The contribution of the blank in the ultraviolet region of the spectrum is by no means a negligible proportion of the actual measurement and it is also rather variable.

To diminish further both the magnitude and the variability of the blank, the film may be pre-washed by allowing suitable solvents to ascend the film as in the development of a chromatogram (this is discussed in further detail in Chapter 3, section 3). Alternatively, the adsorbent may be treated with a solvent in a Soxhlet extractor before the films are prepared.

TABLE 24. COEFFICIENT OF VARIATION FOR VARIOUS SPECTROPHOTOMETRIC ANALYSES

Authors	Compound	λ (nm)	No. of observations	Coefficient of Variation
89	biphenyl	248	57	3·5%
90	biphenyl	248	9	9·3%
91	reserpin	268	18	5·5%
	rescinnamine	268	18	3·8%
92	methyl p-hydroxy benzoate	256	13	3·2%
	propyl p-hydroxy benzoate	256	14	4·8%

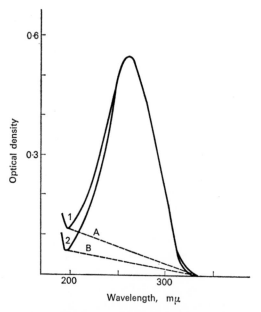

FIG. 21. Elimination of adsorbent impurity contribution in spectroscopy of thin layer chromatography isolates. Optical density of propyl p-hydroxybenzoate: 1, sample recovered from chromatogram; 2, original sample. The gap between the base-lines A and B represents the contribution of the impurities originating in the absorbent.[92]

Gänshirt and Morianz[92] tested an alternative method for eliminating the optical contribution from the adsorbent. Pure solvent was used as the spectroscopic blank instead of an extract from the adsorbent, and the absorption spectrum was recorded over a wide waveband. Subsequently a line was drawn across the base of the absorption peak (Fig. 21) and it was assumed that the gap between this line and the corresponding line for the unchromatographed compound represents the optical density curve of the impurity from the adsorbent. The contribution of the sample is measured from the maximum to this baseline.

The coefficient of variation for the methyl and propyl esters of p-hydroxy benzoic acid were ±3·2% (13 determinations) and ±3·8% (14 determinations) (Table 24).

Another way of diminishing the effect of the impurity in the absorbent is to ignore the specific chromophore of the test compound and to subject it to a reaction which will enable the optical density measurements to be made at a longer wavelength. The longer the wavelength, the less will be the optical contribution of the adsorbent impurity. It is, of course, necessary to verify that the system obeys Beer's Law.

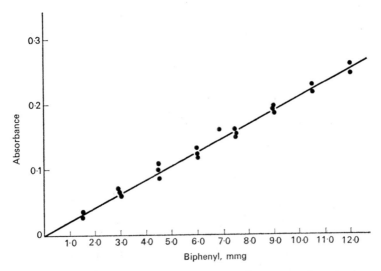

FIG. 22. Ultraviolet spectroscopy of thin-layer chromatography extracts. Calibration curve for mg diphenyl from ultraviolet absorbance readings taken at 248 mμ. Extraction from the silicic acid was with 5 ml 95% alcohol throughout.[135]

Stanley et al.[135] have discussed in some detail the application of thin-layer chromatography combined with ultraviolet spectroscopy to the analysis of a known mixture of diphenyl, mixed hydrocarbons and a group of mixed oxygenated compounds which appear as three separate spots on the chromatogram. They report an excellent correlation between weights of diphenyl in synthetic samples spotted on to the plate and the absorbance in the ultraviolet at 248 mμ obtained in solvent extracts of the diphenyl containing area of the plate (see Fig. 22).

Vioque and Holman[136] have described experimental details for the determination of individual components of mixtures of known esters. They separate the esters on a silica gel plate; the zones corresponding to different types of esters are scraped from the plate and the esters extracted with diethyl ether. The iron hydroxamate complexes of the individual pure esters are then formed and estimated spectrophotometrically at 520 mμ. Typical recoveries obtained by this procedure are quoted on page 68.

Optical Densiometric Analysis[88]

Hefendehl[93] (1960) discovered that there is a linear relationship between the "extinction area" of a spot on the densiometric trace of a chromatogram and the weight of material

	mole %	
	added	found
methyl palmitate	58·8	59·0 ± 2·5
methyl 6-hydroxystearate	19·0	18·6 ± 1·4
methyl 9:10-dihydroxystearate	22·2	22·4 ± 1·5

in the spot. To make the chromatoplate translucent he sprayed the adsorbent with an ethereal solution of paraffin and then measured the optical density of the chromatogram as a function of the distance from the origin (Fig. 23). The area under the peak, measured to the dashed baseline, is a linear function of the weight of material in the spot. Scanning photodensitometers for thin-layer chromatography plates are now commercially available. The extinction area varies from one chromatogram to another so a calibration standard is required for each chromatogram prepared.

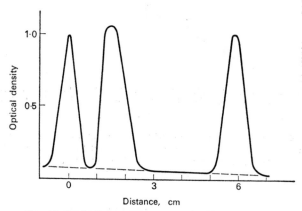

FIG. 23. Optical densiometric analysis of thin-layer chromatograms.[88] Optical density of a chromatogram as a function of the distance from the origin.

Methods Based on Spot Size[88]

As in the densiometric analysis, methods based on spot size avoid all the difficulties connected with the recovery of the sample and with the extraction of impurities from the adsorbent. An additional advantage is that they may be applied with equal facility to adsorption or partition chromatograms. To illustrate the methods the determination of the cholesterol content of wool wax alcohols by adsorption chromatography will be described.

A series of standard solutions of cholesterol was prepared by serial dilution. Equal volumes (2 μl) of a solution of known concentration of the sample and of each of the standard solutions were spotted on to the adsorbent alternatively. For high accuracy a micrometer syringe should be used, but also a capillary pipette (Drummond Microcap) could be used. After the chromatogram had been developed in cyclohexane containing 10% acetone, the solvent-free adsorbent was sprayed with sulphuric acid and the chromoplate was warmed. The result is shown in Fig. 24.

An approximate evaluation of the cholesterol content of the sample is possible visually. Thus the area of the unknown cholesterol spot lies between standards No. 2 and No. 3, and rather nearer to No. 3. Hence the amount of cholesterol in the sample spot lies between 5 μg and 10 μg, the most acceptable value being 9 μg which is equivalent to 30% of the sample.

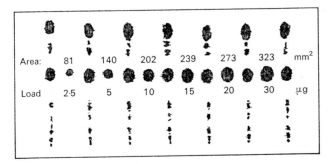

FIG. 24. Quantitative evaluation of thin-layer chromatoplates based on spot size.[88] Photograph of a set of cholesterol standards interspersed with the same sample of wool wax alcohols. Adsorbent: silicagel G. Solvent: cyclohexane/acetone (9 : 1). Chromogenic reagent: sulphuric acid.

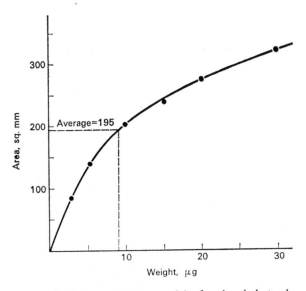

FIG. 25. Plot of area versus weight for the cholesterol standards shown in Fig. 24. Purdy and Truter.[95]

Normally the areas of the spots are determined by laying a sheet of tracing paper over the chromatogram, tracing the outlines of the spots and subsequently measuring the areas on the traces, but in this example the areas were measured from an enlarged photograph. The cholesterol content of the sample may now be evaluated graphically[94] or arithmetically.[95]

In Seher's method[94] the observation for the standards are plotted in the form area versus weight (Fig. 25), and the weight corresponding to the mean area of the unknown samples is read from the graph. The weight of cholesterol is 9·2 μg per spot, corresponding to 30·7% of the sample.

Purdy and Truter[95] discovered that the square root of the area is a linear function of the logarithm of the weight of material in the spot. Statistical tests by these workers showed that the goodness of fit with their relationship is more satisfactory than for any of the earlier proposals.

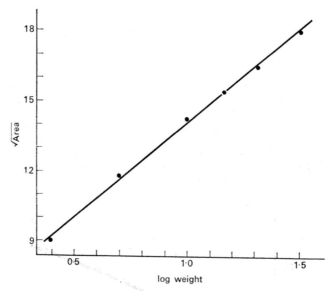

FIG. 26. Plot of the data in Figs. 24 and 25 in the form $\sqrt{}$ area versus log weight. After Purdy and Truter.[95]

The advantages of using the linear relation between $\sqrt{A}$ and log W are that the experimental work can be substantially reduced, and statistical evaluation of the accuracy is possible. Only two standard solutions, one of which is prepared from the other by dilution, are required to determine the equation of a straight line. Equal volumes of the two standard solutions and the test solution are chromatographed simultaneously, and the weight of the compound in the sample is calculated from the equation:

$$\log W = \log W_s + \left(\frac{\sqrt{A} - \sqrt{A_s}}{\sqrt{A_s} - \sqrt{A_d}}\right) \log D$$

where the subscripts s and d refer to the standard and the diluted standard, and D is the dilution factor.

The six standards shown in Fig. 24 can be used to test the validity of the relation $\sqrt{A} \propto \log W$ (Fig. 26). For a statistical determination of the accuracy of the process, any standard may be taken as the "unknown" and its value may be calculated from any combination of two from the remaining five standards. Altogether ten separate combinations are possible for each "unknown". As there are six possible "unknowns" the entire data represent 60 separate values which are summarized in Table 25.

Purdy and Truter[88] conclude that the spectrophotometric method in which the extinction coefficients are first calibrated is most accurate, but it is only marginally better than a carefully performed spot-area analysis. The spectrophotometric method, as used by most workers, is less accurate than is generally believed. In the absence of adequate data a fair assessment of the optical densiometric method was not possible.

Having regard to the important features of an analysis, namely, its accuracy, the time and the special equipment it requires, there can be little doubt that the simple elegance of the spot-area method must recommend it as the first choice in the view of these workers.

TABLE 25. STATISTICAL TESTS ON THE DATA FROM FIG. 24

"Unknown"	Found (μg) (mean of 10)	Known (μg)	Δ (%)	Coefficient of variation
1	2·30	2·50	8·0	
2	5·30	5·00	6·0	
3	10·50	10·00	5·0	6·6%
4	14·30	15·00	4·0	
5	19·90	20·00	0·5	
6	29·60	30·00	1·8	

Attaway et al.[96] discuss in some detail the application of the optical density and spectrophotometric methods discussed above to the determination of esters by thin-layer chromatography. They used glass plates coated with silica gel G. Chromatoplates were developed by the ascending technique, using benzene or trifluoro-trichloroethane:methylene chloride 60:40 as developing solvents.

Detection sprays were mixtures of potassium permanganate and sulphuric acid and also vanillin in 96% sulphuric acid.

To minimize differences between individual chromatoplates, standard R_f values of the esters were computed using citronellal as an internal standard.

Quantitative estimations were based on optical density measurement using a densitometer for spots of lowest concentration, 0·5–5 nl (nanolitre) per spot and on spectrophotometric measurements for spots of higher concentration. Only those compounds reacting with vanillin/H_2SO_4 could be studied accurately with the transmission densitometer as the spots formed with $KMnO_4/H_2SO_4$ could not be measured by the light transmission method. The spectrophotometric procedure was not only limited to materials sensitive to vanillin, but could only be used satisfactorily with a portion of the vanillin-sensitive substances. Figure 27 shows a typical curve obtained by reading a set of varying concentration spots using the densitometer. The graph is seen to be linear to a concentration of about 5 nl/spot. Plots of data from spectrophotometric measurement give a straight line up to a relatively high concentration. However, as mentioned above, not all compounds could be measured by this method. The colorimetric procedure involved the careful removal of the spot from the chromatoplate 4–6 hr after spraying. The coloured silica gel was placed in a 12-ml centrifuge tube and 2 ml of Skellysolve B was added with stirring to elute the colour. The colour was centrifuged to separate the silica gel and then decanted into a cell for the colorimetric reading taking care to avoid evaporation. No difficulties were encountered with geranyl, neryl, linalyl, and other esters giving green spots. However, the blue colour obtained from carvyl, terpinyl, and some other esters faded too rapidly in Skellysolve B solution for use in quantitative measurement. The yellow colour from anthranilate esters disappeared immediately on contact with this solvent. A number of solvents were investigated to determine if these undesirable effects could be minimized. However, only acetone gave improved results, the blue colours fading much more slowly in this solvent. Unfortunately, the yellow colours from anthranilate esters disappeared instantly with all solvents tested. All colours were totally insoluble in both benzene and carbon tetrachloride.

Peifer[97] has discussed the determination of cholesterol by thin-layer chromatography on silica gel G, silicic acid, alumina and Florisil coated plates. He used 25% perchloric acid as detection reagent and heated the plates to develop colour. Transmission photodensitometry was used for quantitative estimation. Figures 28 and 29 illustrate some typical results obtained by Peifer.

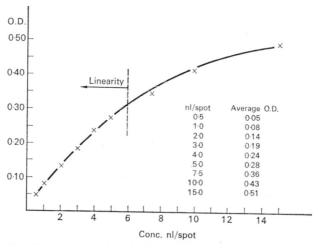

FIG. 27. Quantitative densitometric estimation of carvylacetate spots on thin-layer plate. Spots visualized with concentrated sulphuric acid–vanillin spray.[96]

Waggon et al.[98] describe a semi-quantitative method based on thin-layer chromatography for the determination in polyethylene of Ionol (2,6-di-tert-butyl-p-cresol) and Santonox R (4,4'-thio-bis-6-tert-butyl-m-cresol) in amounts down to 0·03%.

Below are described quantitative procedures for determining, respectively, in polyethylene, Santonox R (4,4'-thio-bis-6-tert-butyl-m-cresol), and the ultraviolet stabilizer Cyasorb UV 531 (2-hydroxy-4-n-octoxybenzophenone) in amounts down to 20 ppm in polymer with an accuracy of ± 20% of the determined amount.

Determination of Santonox R

Polyethlyene extraction procedure

Accurately weigh 5 g of polymer into a 500-ml round-bottomed flask. Add 65 ml of toluene and heat on a boiling water bath for 90 min using a reflux condenser.

Remove the flask from the water bath and immediately pour 85 ml of absolute ethanol down the condenser to precipitate the dissolved polyethylene from the hot toluene solution. Allow the flask to cool to room temperature, remove the condenser, stopper the flask and

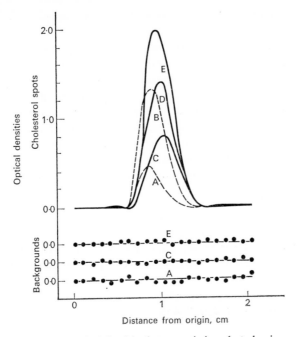

FIG. 28. Optical densities by transmission photodensi-tometry of cholesterol spots on silica gel G coated microscope slides. Each sample was dissolved in 10 μl n-hexane. All density measurements were corrected for irregularities in the background as shown for three of these curves at the bottom of the graph. The amounts of cholesterol were: A, 10 μg; B, 40 μg; C, 20 μg; D, 40 μg; and E, 60 μg.[97]

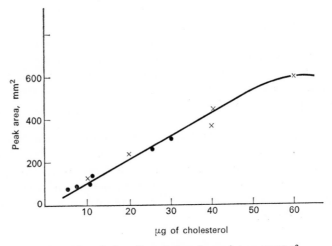

FIG. 29. Relation of area below the peak to amount of cholesterol $\times$ peak areas of the curves of Fig. 28.[97]

shake well. Filter the solution through a No. 42 Whatman filter paper into a 250-ml beaker. Wash the flask and residue with a further 100 ml of ethanol.

Evaporate the toluene/ethanol solution almost to dryness on a boiling water bath with the aid of a stream of nitrogen and finally to dryness using only the nitrogen stream. If more polymer is precipitated during the evaporation, refilter the solution into smaller beaker. Wash the residue into a 2-ml volumetric flask with chloroform and make up to the mark.

Santonox R is extracted from polyethylene by precipitation of the polymer with ethanol from a hot toluene solution as described above. The extract is evaporated to dryness, dissolved in chloroform and an aliquot applied to a thin-layer plate and the chromatogram developed. The concentration of Santonox R in the polyethylene is estimated by visually comparing the intensity of the spot obtained with corresponding spots from known quantities of Santonox R.

Apparatus

Thin-layer chromatography tank.
Thin-layer plate 20 cm × 20 cm, pre-coated with a 250 μ layer of Merck GF254 silica gel, U.K. distributors, Anderman & Co. Ltd., Battlebridge House, Tooley St., London, S.E.1.
Hypodermic syringe – 25 μl capacity.
Ultraviolet lamp – wavelength 254 mμ.

Reagents

Chloroform, Analar, British Drug Houses.
Petroleum ether, 40/60 Analar, British Drug Houses.
Santonox R (4,4′-thio-bis-3-methyl 6-t-butyl phenol)
Ethyl acetate, Analar, British Drug Houses.
2,6-dibromo-p-benzoquinone-4-chlorimime, British Drug Houses.
Sodium tetraborate (borax), Analar, British Drug Houses.

Place 20 μl of the chloroform of the polyethylene sample as a spot on a thin-layer plate. Also apply 20 μl aliquots of standard solutions of Santonox R in chloroform, 0·05%, 0·04%, 0·03% w/v. Develop the chromatogram to a distance of 10 cm in a chromatography tank containing petroleum ether (40:60)/ethyl acetate (5:1 v/v mixture) as the eluent.

Inspect the plate under ultraviolet light (254 mμ) and compare the intensity of the Santonox R spot from the polyethylene extract with the intensities of the standard spots. If the spot is of lower intensity than that of the 0·03% w/v standard then a new chromatogram should be developed using standards 0·025%, 0·015% and 0·005% w/v of Santonox R in chloroform.

Visually compare under ultraviolet lamp the intensity of the spot from the polyethylene extract with the standard spots and thus estimate the percentage level of Santonox R in the chloroform solution. Spray the thin-layer plate with a 2% w/v ethanol solution of 2,6-dibromo-p-benzoquinone-4-chlorimine. Allow the thin-layer plate to dry and re-spray using a 2% w/v aqueous solution of borax. Re-estimate the amount of Santonox R present in the chloroform solution by visually comparing the purple spots produced.

Calculation

Santonox R from 5 g of polyethylene is concentrated into a 2 ml chloroform solution.

Thus the wt. % of Santonox R in high density polyethylene:

$= \frac{2}{5} \times$ the level of Santonox R present in the 2-ml chloroform solution (as determined by thin-layer chromatography in % w/v).

Determination of UV 531

This method describes a thin-layer chromatographic spectroscopic procedure for the determination of ultraviolet Cyasorb UV 531 in high density polyethylene extracts. No interference is encountered from a number of additives, viz. dilauryl thiodipropionate (DLTP), 330, Ionol CP, Topanol CA, Santonox R, Polygard (TNPP).

UV 531 is extracted from the polymer by precipitation of the polymer with ethanol from a hot toluene solution as described above. An aliquot of the extract is applied to a thin-layer plate and chromatographed. The zone corresponding to UV 531 is removed from the plate and extracted with ethanol. The concentration of UV 531 is determined by measuring the ultraviolet absorption peak near 295 mμ in ethanol solution and referring to a prepared calibration graph.

Apparatus

Thin-layer chromatography tank.

Thin-layer plate 20 cm × 20 cm pre-coated with a 250 μ layer of GF$_{245}$ silica gel, U.K. distributors, Anderman & Co. Ltd., Battlebridge House, Tooley St., London, S.E.1.

Hamilton syringe (to measure 25 μl).

Ultraviolet lamp (wavelength 254 mμ).

Sintered glass filter sticks, $\frac{1}{2}$ diameter.

10-ml standard flasks.

Ultraviolet spectrophotometer.

3-cm silica spectrophotometer cells.

Reagents

Methylene chloride.

Chloroform A.R.

Cyasorb UV 531 ex Cyanamid Ltd.

Standard UV 531 solution, 0·2% w/v in chloroform, for use as a "marker" to locate correct position of UV 531 on plate.

Standard UV 531 polymer blends—prepare by milling a series of blends of 0·05, 0·1, 0·2, 0·3, 0·4 and 0·5% w/w UV 531 in additive-free polyethylene powder.

To calibrate the procedure, weigh out 0·5 g of each of the standard polymer–UV 531 blends and 0·5 to 1·0 g of the unknown polyethylene sample, and put each through the polyethylene solvent extraction procedure.

Apply 25-μl portions of each of the standard polymer extracts and the sample extract to the base line of a thin-layer plate in the form of a spot, keeping the spot size at a minimum by means of a stream of nitrogen. Develop the chromatogram to a distance of 10 cm in a chromatography tank using methylene chloride as eluant. Remove the plate from the tank and allow the solvent to evaporate.

Inspect the plate under ultraviolet light (254 mμ) and locate UV 531 as a dark blue spot. Mark with a pointed marker the zones corresponding to the UV 531 in the standards and the sample and also an equivalent blank area of silica gel.

Carefully scrape the silica gel zones from the plate and transfer to separate sintered glass filter columns. Extract the UV 531 from each with absolute ethanol into a 10-ml standard flask and finally make to volume.

Measure the optical density at 295 mμ of the standard and sample extracts against the gel blank extract in the reference cell in 3-cm silica cells.

Plot a calibration curve for nett optical density at 295 mμ against micrograms UV 531 in final solution (10 ml). Hence, deduce the concentration of UV 531 in the unknown polyethylene sample.

Column chromatography has been applied with some success by Campbell and Wize[99] to the determination of known phenolic antioxidants in polyethylene. This method is applicable to the analysis of mixtures of Santowhite powder (4,4'-butylidene-bis-(6-tert-

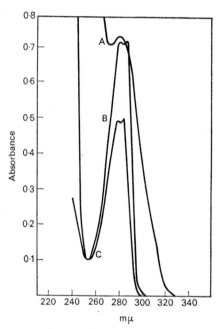

Fig. 30. The ultraviolet spectra of some antioxidants. A, Santonox R (0·0368 g/l. in methanol). B, Santowhite powder (0·0585 g/l. in methanol). C, B.H.T. (0·052 g/l. in chloroform).[99]

butyl-*m*-cresol)) with B.H.T. (butylated hydroxy toluene) and mixtures of Santonox R (4,4'-thio-bis-(6-tert-butyl-*m*-cresol)) with B.H.T. (butylated hydroxy toluene) in the concentration range 0·01–0·3%. This method should be equally applicable to other types of polyolefins.

Total additives are first removed from the polyethylene sample by extraction with warm chloroform. The chloroform extract is then transferred to a column comprising a slurry of aluminium oxide in the same solvent.

Elution with chloroform removes B.H.T. only as the first fraction. Continued elution of the column with solutions of 10% water in methanol removes Santowhite powder or

Santonox R as a separate pure fraction, free from B.H.T. Additives can then be determined in the respective extracts after they have been made up to a standard volume with solvent by ultraviolet spectroscopy.

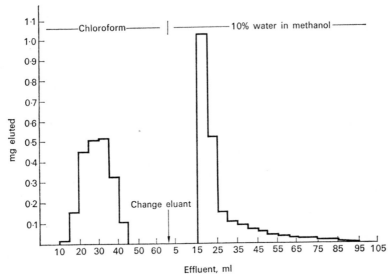

FIG. 31. Elution chromatogram of B.H.T. and Santonox R.[99]

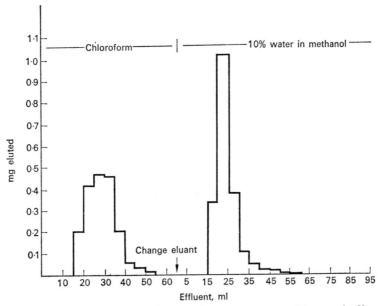

FIG. 32. Elution chromatogram of B.H.T. and Santowhite powder.[99]

Campbell and Wize[99] calculated specific absorptivities from the slope of linear absorbance versus concentration plots for B.H.T. in chloroform, Santowhite powder, and Santonox R in 10% water in methanol. The ultraviolet spectra of the antioxidants are depicted in Fig. 30.

Typical elution chromatograms which show the separation of mixtures of B.H.T.–Santonox R and B.H.T.–Santowhite powder are depicted in Figs. 31 and 32 respectively. It is noted that the water–methanol effluent front elutes the bulk of the Santonox R or Santowhite powder. A large error would result if some of the first part of the aqueous methanol fraction were discarded.

Campbell and Wize[99] verified their procedure by analysing polyethylene samples containing known amounts of antioxidants. The analytical results are cited in Table 26.

TABLE 26. ANALYSIS OF SOME STANDARD POLYETHYLENE SAMPLES BY COMBINED COLUMN CHROMATOGRAPHY/ULTRAVIOLET SPECTROSCOPY

B.H.T.			Santowhite powder			Santonox R		
% added	% found	% re-covered	% added	% found	% re-covered	% added	% found	% re-covered
0·270	0·265	98·0	0·260	0·264	101·3	—	—	—
0·263	0·260	98·8	—	—	—	0·257	0·248	96·5
0·0513	0·0508	99·2	0·253	0·249	98·4	—	—	—
0·0535	0·0534	99·8	—	—	—	0·251	0·245	97·5

Some standard samples were prepared by milling weighed amounts of B.H.T., Santowhite powder, and Santonox R in polyethylene at 130°. The analyses of these samples agreed satisfactorily for Santowhite powder and Santonox R, but the B.H.T. concentrations were approximately 30% low. A feasible explanation would be that B.H.T. has a greater volatility than the others, and some B.H.T. was lost due to evaporation during the hot milling process.

CHAPTER 3

APPLICATION OF CHROMATOGRAPHY FOLLOWED BY SPECTROSCOPY TO THE IDENTIFICATION AND DETERMINATION OF UNKNOWN ADDITIVE MIXTURES

A NECESSARY prerequisite of the methods discussed in Chapters 1 and 2 is that the analyst has a full knowledge of all the types of additive present in the polymer. This is necessary so that in selecting a method for determining a particular constituent, due allowances can be made for other types of additive constituents present or of any decomposition products of additives present. Whilst this information might be to hand if an analyst is examining materials of known origin, this would not always be so. In such cases, which are the subject matter of Chapters 3 and 4, it is mandatory that the first step must be to completely identify the additives present, before any consideration can be given to the problem of selecting or devising a method of quantitative analysis for any constituent present in the polymer.

The problem resolves itself into the preparation of a total solvent extract of the polymer in which all additives are completely recovered, followed by separation of the mixture into pure single components by a suitable form of chromatography and, finally, by identification of each separated pure component by suitable means, usually involving visible infrared, ultraviolet, mass or nuclear magnetic resonance spectroscopy and perhaps micro-analysis for elements present. Only after this stage can the details of the quantitative determination of particular polymer constituents be considered.

It is advisable when commencing the analysis of a polymer for unknown additives to determine first its content of various non-metallic and metallic elements. Any element found to be present must be accounted for in the subsequent examination for, and identification of, additives. Hence, elemental analysis reduces the possibility of overlooking any additive which contains elements other than carbon, hydrogen and oxygen.

The analytical methods used to determine elements should be sufficiently sensitive to determine about 10 ppm of an element in the polymer, i.e. should be able to detect in a polymer, a substance present at 0·01% and containing down to 10% of the element in question.

This requirement is met for almost all the important elements by use of optical emission spectrography and X-ray fluorescence spectrometry. Using these two techniques, all metals and non-metals down to an atomic number of 15 (phosphorus) can be determined at the required concentrations. Nitrogen is determinable at these levels by micro-Kjeldahl digestion techniques.

79

Apart from gas chromatography, discussed in Chapter 4, three forms of chromatography are worthy of serious consideration for the separation of additive mixtures, viz.
column, paper and thin-layer chromatography. Of these, thin-layer chromatography is by
far the most useful general technique and this is discussed in Chapter 3, section 3. Firstly,
however, column and paper chromatography will be discussed in Chapter 3, sections 1 and 2.

3.1   Column Chromatography

Thin-layer chromatography often provides enough of each of the individual polymer
additives in a sufficiently high state of purity to enable them to be identified by spectroscopic
methods. However, if insufficient sample is provided by this technique then larger quantities in the 50–500 mg range can be obtained by scaling up the separation on to a column.
Column chromatography is more time-consuming than thin-layer chromatography, therefore the latter technique should be used in preliminary experiments aimed at finding suitable
adsorbents and development solvents for achieving a satisfactory separation. These conditions can then usually be translated to a column without difficulty. Similarly, the thin-layer
technique is useful as a rapid method of monitoring the purity of fractions obtained in
column separations.

Successful separations can often be achieved on columns of activated silica gel by successive elution of the sample on the column with a range of solvents of increasing polarity.

A hexane solution of the sample is transferred to the top of the column of gel which has
been filled with the same solvent. The column is then successively eluted with n-hexane,
mixtures of n-hexane and benzene (or toluene), neat benzene (or toluene), mixtures of benzene (or toluene) and absolute ethanol (or acetone), and finally absolute ethanol (or acetone).
Only solvents of suitable purity should be used in this work, e.g. spectroscopic or chromatographic grades.

This process provides a series of fractions in the collector from which particular groups
of fractions can be used for further evaluation. In some cases, of course, some of the fractions will consist of the low molecular weight component of the original polymer.

One of the difficulties of column chromatography is the problem of identifying the
fractions in which the separated compounds are concentrated. This can be achieved by the
laborious process of examining all the fractions, for example by infrared or ultraviolet
spectroscopy or by evaporating to dryness and weighing the residues; or by the less laborious
process of monitoring the effluent as it leaves the chromatographic column so that solute-
containing fractions from the fraction collector can be picked out from the fractions which
do not contain any substances. Several types of effluent monitors are available, based on the
measurement of the ultraviolet absorption, conductivity, etc. (LKB Stockholm). These have
the disadvantage of being too specific for dealing with mixtures of compounds of unknown
type. For example, compounds which do not either absorb in the ultraviolet or ionize would
be missed using these detectors. The most useful general purpose monitors are those based
on the measurement of refractive index (the Waters detector) and on thermal effects (the
Japanese Electron Optics Laboratory JLC 2A universal recording chromatograph, see
Fig. 33).

The latter instrument operates on the principle that as each separated compound moves
down the column it is accompanied by heat of adsorption and desorption due to interaction
between solute molecules and the stationary phases. These heat pockets (i.e. separated
compounds) are detected by a thermistor at the column outlet and recorded on a strip chart

Fig. 33. The JLC 2A universal recording chromatograph. Reproduced by kind permission of Pergamon Press Ltd.[16]

which can be operated in conjunction with a fraction collector. Thus, separated fractions can be readily located and bulked if necessary for further examination.

The writer has used this apparatus to separate up to 200 mg of antioxidants from each other using a silica gel column. Santonox R (4,4′-thio-bis-(3-methyl-6-tert-butyl phenol) and Ionol CP were easily separated on this scale using benzene as the development solvent. Topanol CA and dilauryl thiodipropionate were well resolved using cyclohexane:ethyl acetate (9:1 v/v).

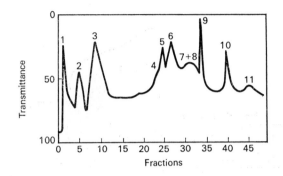

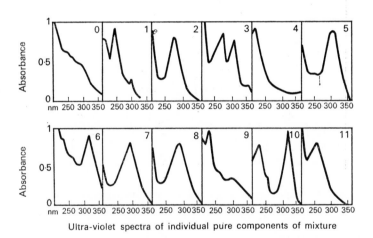

Ultra-violet spectra of individual pure components of mixture

FIG. 34. Column chromatography on alumina of antioxidants accelerators and plasticizers in rubber extracts and ultraviolet spectra of separated compounds.[100]

Adsorbents other than silica gel can be used for the separation of mixtures of polymer additives; thus Fiorenza et al.[100] have described a technique based on column chromatography on neutral alumina for the separation of antioxidants, plasticizers, etc., in rubber extracts (Fig. 34). They detected the separated compounds by monitoring the effluent with a LKB 254 mμ ultraviolet detector (Fig. 35). In this procedure a carbon tetrachloride solution of the sample is applied to an alumina column wetted with the same solvent and the column is successively eluted with carbon tetrachloride, mixtures of carbon tetrachloride and benzene, benzene, mixtures of benzene and absolute ethanol, and finally, ethanol. Separations were carried out on a scale to provide enough of each separated compound for the preparation of infrared and ultraviolet spectra.

A synthetic rubber adsorbent was used by Berger et al.[12] to separate antioxidants. The stationary phase (Silastic 181) was applied to the column as a suspension in light petroleum and separation carried out with a mobile phase of 21% v/v acetone in water. Campbell and Wize[99] used an alumina column to separate phenolic antioxidants with chloroform followed by 10% v/v water in ethanol. They used a Gilston Medical Electronics ultraviolet scanner coupled to a recorder to monitor the effluent stream.

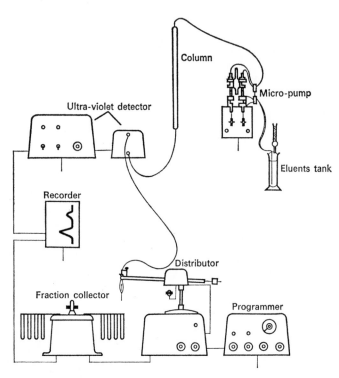

FIG. 35. Experimental system employed by Fiorenza et al.[100] in column chromatography of rubber extracts.

A separatory analytical scheme based on column chromatography was reported by Parker,[101] in which aliquots of the sample solution were chromatographed on seven alumina columns, each with a different mobile phase. From the position of the components on the various columns after a suitable elution time and from the colours obtained with specific detecting agents, he claimed to be able to obtain almost unambiguous identification of antioxidants.

Bellamy et al.[115] have discussed in detail the identification of antioxidants in rubber vulcanizates.

They first chromatographed the sample extract on an alumina column. Separated compounds were detected on the column by ultraviolet light and/or by extruding the moist column from the tube and streaking a narrow band down the side of the column with various chromogenic reagents such as sulphuric acid, 1% ammonium vanadate in sulphuric acid,

1% potassium dichromate in sulphuric acid or 1:3 v/v nitric:sulphuric acid. He discusses the behaviour on the column of certain individual antioxidants such as phenyl-alpha-naphthylamine, phenyl-beta-naphthylamine, Agerite White, Neozone HF, Flectol H, and

TABLE 27. COMPOUNDS STUDIED BY PARKER AND BERRIMAN[117]

Accelerator or antioxidant	Reputed composition
Group A	
Vulcafor DOTG	di-*o*-tolyl guanidine
Vulcafor DPG	diphenyl guanidine
Vulcafor TPG	triphenyl guanidine
Vulcafor TC	thiocarbanilide
Vulcafor MBT	mercaptobenzthiazole
Vulcafor MBTS	dibenzthiazolyl-2-disulphide
Vulcafor TMT	tetramethylthiuram disulphide
Vulcafor MS	tetramethylthiuram monosulphide
Vulcafor TET	tetraethylthiuram disulphide
Santocure	2-benzthiazolyl-N'-cyclohexyl sulphenamide
Neozone A (PAN)	phenyl α-naphthylamine
Neozone D (PBN)	phenyl β-naphthylamine
Agerite White	sym-di-β-naphthyl-*p*-phenylenediamine
MTD	*m*-toluylene diamine
DPPD	sym-diphenyl-*p*-phenylenediamine
Group B	
ZMC	zinc dimethyldithiocarbamate
Vulcafor ZDC	zinc diethyldithiocarbamate
Vulcafor ZNBC	zinc di-n-butyldithiocarbamate
Vulcafor MA	formaldehyde-aniline condensation product
Vulcafor RN	acetaldehyde-aniline condensation product
Nonox NS	phenol-aldehyde-ketone
Nonox S	aldol-naphthylamine condensation product
Flectol H	polymerized trimethyl dihydroquinoline
Perflectol	(found Flectol H and DPPD)
Neozone C	(found *m*-toluylene diamine (MTD) and phenyl α-naphthylamine)
Neozone HF	(found phenyl β-naphthylamine and sym-di-phenyl-*p*-phenylenediamine (DPPD))
Ureka White	(found MBT and quanidine derivative)
Vulcafor DAU	(found TET and MBTS)
Vulcafor DAW	(found MBT and quanidine derivative)
Vulcafor DHC	(found MBT and ZDC)
Vulcafor F	(found MBTS and guanidine derivative)
Vulcafor FN	(found MBTS and guanidine derivative)

Agerite Stalite. These compounds were generally easily eluted from an alumina column with 1:99 ethanol:benzene and hence could be easily separated from other less mobile constituents of the original mixture.

Mann[116] extended the work of Bellamy *et al.*[115] by utilizing infrared and ultraviolet spectroscopy for the examination of individual components of vulcanizate extracts, mainly antioxidants and accelerators, after separation from all other compounds present by column chromatography. He used a similar chromatographic technique to Bellamy. After chromatography, portions of the eluate were evaporated to dryness and examined by infrared

spectroscopy. Mixtures of the following types of compounds were in many cases successfully dealt with; thiazoles, dithiocarbamates, thiurams, xanthates, guanidines, aldehyde
amine compounds and various types of amine and phenolic antioxidants. Contrary to
Bellamy,[115] Mann[116] showed that weak adsorption on alumina is not a characteristic
feature of antioxidants. Some of these compounds are relatively strongly adsorbed on
alumina and require for desorption ethyl alcohol:benzene mixtures nearer to 5:95 v/v
rather than the 1:99 v/v mixture proposed by Bellamy.[115]

Mann[116] concludes that although infrared methods offer a reasonable solution to the
problem of the qualitative analysis of vulcanizates for accelerators and antioxidants, it is
unlikely that they could be made quantitative. He suggested that ultraviolet spectroscopy
would be more amenable to quantitative analysis and more sensitive for the determination
of accelerators and antioxidants.

Parker and Berriman[117] explored the chromatographic behaviour on silica gel/Celite
packed columns of 32 accelerators and antioxidants of the type used in vulcanized rubber
formulations. Methylene chloride was used as sample solvent. They identified separated
compounds by viewing the developed column in ultraviolet light, by application of various
chromogenic streaking reagents to the extruded chromatographic column and by examination by ultraviolet spectroscopy. Parker[117] claims that silica gel/Celite mixtures as adsorbent
have certain advantages over alumina as advocated by Bellamy[115] and by Mann.[116] Thus,
it has a weak adsorptive power for accelerators and antioxidants, which permits the chromatography of labile compounds without decomposition. Also, silica gel/Celite is claimed to
be more suitable for the application of a wide variety of streak reagents, and is more
amenable to the quantitative recovery of adsorbates from the column.

Table 27 lists the types of compounds discussed by Parker and Berriman.[117]

A number of colour reactions for accelerators and antioxidants which have been reported in the literature are shown in Table 28. Many of these are suitable for application as
streak reagents. Table 29 lists the reagents used for the detection of the single Group A
compounds of Table 27.

The limiting sensitivities of the various streak reagents used for detecting the compounds
listed in Table 27 were obtained by developing increasing quantities of each of the compounds on 1-cm columns by the procedures described below. In most cases the smallest
detectable quantity corresponded to 0·05 mg on a 1-cm column under the conditions quoted.

For qualitative work columns of silica gel–Celite mixture 1 cm in diameter and 15 cm
long were employed by Parker and Berriman.[117] 1·0-mg quantities of most of the compounds
formed well-defined zones on such columns and in most cases very strong streak tests were
obtained with this quantity. Methylene chloride readily dissolved all the compounds concerned and its developing power was not unduly great. However, it is not suitable for placing
very weakly adsorbed compounds such as the phenyl-naphthylamines. Light petroleum or
carbon tetrachloride is suitable for these compounds. All chlorohydrocarbons were washed
and dried before use as the development of traces of chlorine produced serious decomposition of many solutes. A number of binary solvent mixtures were investigated solvents by
Parker and Berriman.[117] Table 30 presents the adsorption series obtained with the four binary
solvent mixtures which were most fully investigated. The concentration of the more polar
constituent of the development solvent which will produce a convenient development of the
zone is shown against each compound. Where compounds are not completely separated by
one binary developer, a good separation can often be obtained by the use of a different
binary solvent. For example, using mixtures of ethyl acetate and benzene the zone of TMT

TABLE 28. SOME COLORIMETRIC REAGENTS REPORTED IN THE LITERATURE

Reagent	Compounds reacting	Literature reference
$Bi(NO_3)_3$–1% $NaOH$–HNO_3	MBT, thiuram	119
Aq. $Bi(NO_3)_3$ in acetone	MBT	122
$AuCl_3$	DPG	119
Cu oleate in $CHCl_3$	dithiocarbamates	120
Ditto, after Na_2SO_3	thiuram sulphide	120
Co oleate in benzene	DPG, DOTG, o-tolyldiguanide dithiocarbamates, MBT, TMT	124, 125
$CuSO_4$ aq. + acetone, etc.	dithiocarbamates, thiurams, etc.	119, 122, 123
Phenolphthalein	DPG	121
HCl and phenol or α-naphthol	diazoaminobenzene	121
Diazotized p-nitraniline	aromatic amines	128, 121
NaOH and diazotized p-nitraniline	aromatic amines	127
Diazotized sulphanilic acid	aldol naphthylamine	129
Acetic acid or HCl and p-dimethyl-amino benzaldehyde	1-naphthyliminoaldol, PBN	121
p-Phenylenediamine, Br_2 and NH_3	1-naphthyliminoaldol, thiuram	121
p-Phenylenediamine and $FeCl_3$	primary and various amines	128
$FeCl_3$ or $CuCl_2$	aldol-naphthylamine	131
Aq. NaOCl + phenol (3%)	aldehyde-aniline condensation products	125
$SnCl_4$ and amyl nitrite in benzene	diarylamines and naphthylaryl-amines	128
$SnCl_4$ and benzotrichloride in ethylene dichloride	diarylamine-ketone condensation products	128
$SnCl_4$ benzoyl peroxide in benzene	aryl substituted p-phenylene diamines	128
$SnCl_4$ and bromine in ethylene dichloride	aniline-acetone condensation products, etc.	128
H_2SO_4 and trace HNO_3	diphenyl and dinaphthyl p-phenylenediamines	130
H_2SO_4 H_2SO_4 + SeO_3 H_2SO_4 + $K_2S_2O_2$ Conc. HNO_3 Arsenic acid in H_2SO_4 Amm. molybdate in H_3SO_4 10% H_2O_2 in H_2SO_4 H_2SO_4 HNO_3	reactions of 40 commercial anti-oxidants investigated	126
$(NH_4)_2S_2O_8$ in H_2SO_4 0·5% MoO_3 in H_2SO_4 0·5% SeO_2 in H_2SO_4 Acetic acid Acetic acid + bromine 1% ammonium vanadate in conc. H_2SO_4	reactions of 8 commercial anti-oxidants investigated	127
1% potassium dichromate in conc. H_2SO_4 Nitric acid/sulphuric acid 1:3	reactions with 9 commercial anti-oxidants recorded	132

TABLE 29. COLOURS OF STREAKS OBTAINED WITH VARIOUS REAGENTS
(Parker and Berriman[117])

Compound	30% w/v Sodium hypochlorite	5% w/v Aqueous CuSO$_4$·5H$_2$O	5% w/v Bi(NO$_2$)$_3$ in 0·5 N nitric acid	Bismuth nitrate in 0·5 N nitric acid after reduction	5% w/v Aqueous Pb(C$_2$H$_3$O$_2$)$_2$ 3H$_2$O	Aqueous lead acetate after reduction	1% w/v (NH$_4$)VO$_3$ in 60% w/w sulphuric acid	Mixture of conc. HNO$_3$ (1 vol.) and conc. H$_2$SO$_4$ (3 vols.)	0·5% w/v Selenium dioxide in conc. sulphuric acid
Vulcafor DOTG	dark reddish-brown	nil	nil	nil	nil	nil	nil	nil	nil
Vulcafor DPG	dark reddish-brown	nil	nil	nil	nil	nil	nil	nil	nil
Vulcafor TPG	reddish-brown	nil	nil	nil	nil	nil	nil	nil	nil
Vulcafor TC	pale orange on standing	light brown	yellow	yellow	nil	nil	nil	pale violet fades rapidly	nil
Vulcafor MBT	nil	faint yellow	bright chrome-tellow	bright chrome-yellow	lemon-yellow	lemon-yellow	faint green	nil	faint yellow
Vulcafor MBTS	nil	nil	nil	bright chrome-yellow	nil	lemon-yellow	nil	nil	nil
Vulcafor TMT	nil	bright yellow-green	pale lemon-yellow	pale lemon-yellow	nil	nil	v. pale green to faint blue	nil	nil
Vulcafor MS	nil	strong yellow	pale yellow	pale yellow	nil	nil	v. pale green to faint blue	nil	nil

continued on next page

Compound	30% w/v Sodium hypochlorite	5% w/v Aqueous CuSO$_4$.5H$_2$O	5% w/v Bi(NO$_2$)$_3$ in 0.5 N nitric acid	Bismuth nitrate in 0.5 N nitric acid after reduction	5% w/v Aqueous Pb(C$_2$H$_3$O$_2$)$_2$ 3H$_2$O	Aqueous lead acetate after reduction	1% (NH$_4$)VO$_3$ in 60% w/w sulphuric acid	Mixture of conc. HNO$_3$ (1 vol.) and conc. H$_2$SO$_4$ (3 vols.)	0.5% w/v Selenium dioxide in conc. sulphuric acid
Vulcafor TET	nil	bright yellow-green	pale lemon-yellow	pale lemon-yellow	nil	nil	v. pale green to faint blue	nil	nil
Santocure	nil	nil	nil	bright chrome-yellow	nil	lemon-yellow	faint green	nil	nil
PAN	light orange to orange-yellow	nil	nil	nil	nil	nil	prussian blue	dark olive-green	blue on standing
PBN	orange	nil	nil	nil	nil	nil	dark brown	green rapidly turning brown	pale greenish-yellow
Agerite White	orange-pink	nil	pale green or pale blue	nil	nil	nil	dark greenish-blue	mauve	deep blue
MTD	orange-brown	yellow-green	nil	—	nil	—	pink-brown on standing	faint orange	nil
DPPD	pale orange-yellow	nil	light blue	—	nil	—	crimson	magenta	purple

overlaps that of MBT, but with ethyl ether in light petroleum the TMT can be cleanly separated from the MBT.

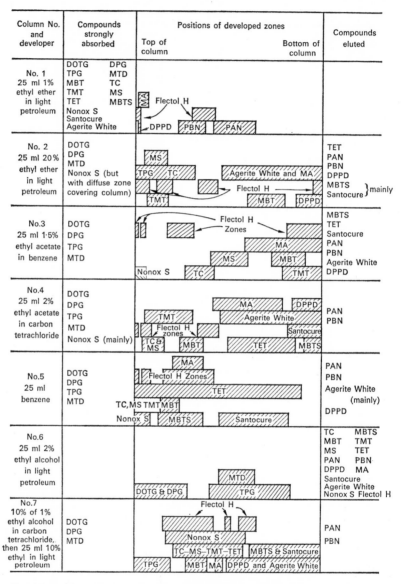

FIG. 36. Positions of zones after development with proposed solvents (Parker and Berriman[11]). Column Chromatography of Accelerators.

With the above chromatographic data as a guide, it was possible to devise a series of chromatographic treatments for obtaining optimum separation of each of the compounds in Table 27 from others giving interfering streak reactions. The developers which were found to be most useful for this purpose are indicated in Fig. 36, which also shows the positions of zones produced on the columns.

Table 30. Adsorption Series of Some Simple Accelerators and Antioxidants from Four Binary Developers (Parker and Berriman[117])

(These data apply when the compounds are placed on the column in methylene chloride: some of these compounds giving diffuse zones under these conditions give tight zones when placed in carbon tetrachloride, e.g. Agerite White.)

Benzene/light petroleum

Adsorption	Compounds
strongly adsorbed	DOTG, DPG, TPG, MDT
100% (slightly developed)	TC, MS
100%	TMT, MBT, TET[b]
100%	MBTS
100%	Santocure
30%	Agerite White[b], DPPD[b]
15%	PBN
	PAN

Ethyl ether/light petroleum

Adsorption	Compounds
100%	DOTG[a]
100%	DPG[a]
50%	MTD, TPG[b]
40%	MS
30%	TMT, TC
20%	MBT
10%	TET
10%	Agerite White[b], DPPD[b], MBTS
10%	Santocure
1%	PBN
1%	PAN

Ethyl acetate/benzene

Adsorption	Compounds
strongly adsorbed	DOTG, DPG
40%	MTD
20%	TPG[b]
$1\frac{1}{2}\%$	TC, MS
$\frac{1}{2}\%$	TMT, MBT, MBTS
$\frac{1}{2}\%$	TET
0%	Santocure
0% eluted	Agerite White[c], DPPD
eluted	PBN
eluted	PAN

Ethyl acetate/carbon tetrachloride

Adsorption	Compounds
strongly adsorbed	DOTG, DPG
50%	MTD
50%	TPG[b]
5–8%	MS
2%	TC, TMT
2%	MBT, TET
1%	Santocure
1%	MBTS
1%	Agerite White[b], DPPD[b], PBN
0%	PAN (mainly eluted with 25 ml)

[a] Diffuse zone at top of column.
[b] Formation of a very diffuse zone covering a large proportion of the column.
[c] Mainly eluted but a pink colour remains on column.
Compounds whose zones overlap are bracketted.

Paraffin wax, mineral jelly and liquid paraffin, all possible constituents of polymer and rubber extracts, are eluted from the column even with light petroleum alone and can thus be separated from accelerators and antioxidants. Any impurities they contain produce little or no colour on the column and do not therefore interfere with the detection of the accelerators and antioxidants. Stearic acid could be detected by streaking the column with bromocresol green indicator solution; the acid changed the colour of the streak from greenish-blue

TABLE 31. COLUMN CHROMATOGRAPHY OF PVC PLASTICIZERS ELUTION SEQUENCE FOR PLASTICIZER MIXTURE

Eluant	Fraction	Plasticizer found
Carbon tetrachloride	1	Cereclor (chlorinated hydrocarbon)
	2	—
	3	—
	4	Mesamoll (alkyl ester of a sulphonic acid)
Carbon tetrachloride/di-isopropyl ether (2%)	5	—
	6	Tritolyl phosphate
	7	Di-n-butyl phthalate
	8	
Carbon tetrachloride/di-isopropyl ether (5%)	9	Di-n-butyl sebacate
	10	—
	11	—
	12	—
Carbon tetrachloride/acetone (2%)	13–16	—
Carbon tetrachloride/acetone (5%)	17	Diethylene glycol
	18	dibenzoate
	19	Abrac "A" (epoxidized vegetable oil)
	20	—
Carbon tetrachloride/acetone (7·5%)	21	—
	22	Polypropylene sebacate
	23	Polypropylene sebacate (trace)
	24	—

to yellow-green. Stearic acid is completely eluted with 20% ethyl alcohol in light petroleum or 20% ethyl ether in light petroleum, (see columns 6 and 2, Fig. 36), and can be recovered quantitatively. With the weaker developers, stearic acid forms wide diffuse zones. It would appear on columns 1, 3, 4, 5 and 7 (Fig. 36), but does not interfere with the identification of the other compounds.

Criddle[81] has described a column chromatographic prodecure for the identification and semi-quantitative determination of plasticizers in PVC. In this procedure the plasticizer is first Soxhlet extracted from 1 to 2 g of PVC sample using anhydrous diethyl ether. Ether is then evaporated from the extract and residual traces of PVC precipitated by the addition of 2 ml absolute ethanol. Following filtration of any polymer, the ethanol is finally evaporated off to provide a PVC free plasticizer extract.

Chromatographic separation of the mixture was achieved on a column comprising equal parts by weight of Celite 545 (100–200 mesh) and silica gel (100–200 mesh), both dried immediately before use for 24 hr at 100–110°C. A mixture of 0·5 g polymer extract and 10 ml carbon tetrachloride was then applied to a carbon tetrachloride wetted column of the Celite–silica gel mixture. Various elution solvents were used by these workers. The column eluate was collected in fractions which were evaporated and weighed. It is seen from Table 31 that good separations were achieved by this method for various plasticizer mixtures.

Selected fractions isolated on the chromatographic column were used for the preparation of infrared spectra which enabled the various components to be identified.

3.2 Paper Chromatography

Wheeler[22] has reviewed the available literature on the applications of paper chromatography in the examination of polymers for antioxidants (Table 32). He points out that, as most antioxidants are highly polar, they cannot be efficiently separated on normal paper except by the use of highly polar mobile phases. Consequently reversed-paper chromatography[102–105] or acetylated papers[38, 106–108] are frequently used to reduce the effects of "tailing".

The detecting spray reagents generally used for antioxidants are either diazotized amines[106, 109] which form coloured products with amines and phenols, or are oxidizing agents, since the oxidation products of antioxidants are generally highly coloured.[110,107, 108, 111] Sometimes the sample solution is treated with the colouring reagent first, and the coloured products are then chromatographed,[38, 112, 113] but multiple spots can be obtained from a single antioxidant in this way as has been demonstrated by Auler.[114]

The work of Zijp is a major contribution to paper chromatographic methods. He devised a comprehensive scheme for the systematic identification of antioxidants and accelerators.[107, 108, 111]

In the part of this scheme relating to antioxidants he uses acetylated paper and two solvent systems, one for basic and one for phenolic acidic constituents. Identification was based mainly on the R_f value of each constituent and on the colours produced by various spray reagents (Tables 33 and 34).

Auler[114] in his detailed survey on the analysis of antioxidants and accelerators was able to reproduce Zijp's work, and in addition he applied the same solvent systems to circular paper chromatography with satisfactory results.

Williamson's work[106] is based on that of Zijp, but employs different solvent systems. Before the chromatography he evaporates the sample extract to dryness at 80°C and dissolves the residue in 96% ethanol. Controlled additions of strontium chloride and ammonia solutions are made to precipitate out fatty acid and other impurities which are then removed by filtration and the clear filtrate examined for antioxidants by paper chromatography.

Delves[137] has described a procedure based on paper chromatography for the identification of nitrogen-containing antioxidants in synthetic aviation turbine oil formulations which with minor modification could be applied to the analysis of plastics. His most successful solvent system for chromatography was dipropylene glycol as the stationary phase and cyclohexane saturated with dipropylene glycol as the mobile phase.

TABLE 32. SEPARATION OF ANTIOXIDANTS BY PAPER CHROMATOGRAPHY (Wheeler)[22]

Substances separated	Stationary phase	Mobile phase	Derivative or treatment	Detection	Comments	Refs.
Gallate's gallic acid butylated hydroxyanisole	7% liquid paraffin on paper	Light petroleum		Ammoniacal silver nitrate	Descending run—4 hr	102 103
Antioxidants in food and fats	Paper	Acetic acid–water (1:4)		0.2% $Fe_2(SO_4)_3$–0.1% $K_3Fe(CN)_6$ (1:1)	Blue spots	110
Amine antioxidants	Paper	Acetic acid–water–acetone (3:6:1)	React with 3-methyl-benzothiazolin-2-one hydrazone HCl/FeCl$_3$ before chromatography	Products coloured		112
Antioxidants	Paper	Not given	Heated under reflux with HCl	Sulphanilic acid–sodium nitrite or ninhydrin		109
Aromatic amines and phenothiazine anti-oxidants	Dipropylene glycol on paper	Cyclohexane saturated with di-propylene glycol		UV light or p-nitro-benzenediazonium fluoroborate	112 μg detected	104
Antioxidants	Whatman acetylated paper No. AC82	Ethanol–benzene–acetylacetone (10:10:1)	Antioxidants extracted from accelerators with ethanol	Potassium p-diazobenzene sulphonate	Ascending against the grain—5 hr	133
Antioxidants	Acetylated Whatman No. 1	Not reported	Extract into ethanol add 4 M NH$_4$OH, 20% SrCl$_2$ and filter			38

continued on next page

Substances separated	Stationary phase	Mobile phase	Derivative or treatment	Detection	Comments	Refs,
Catechols	Whatman No. 1 impregnated with formamide + H₃PO₄, dimethylformamide or liquid paraffin	(a) Isopropyl-ether (b) Chloroform (c) Heptane (d) Heptane–benzene (1:1) (e) 80% Methanol				105
Antioxidants and accelerators	Paper		Coupled with p-diazobenzene sulphonic acid, or alkali	Products coloured		113
Urea-based stabilizers	Paper	Propanol–methanol–water (2:1:1)		p-Dimethylamine-benzaldehyde		34
Basic antioxidants	Acetylated Whatman No. 1	96% Ethanol–benzene (1:1)		4% Benzoyl peroxide in benzene		107 111
Phenolic antioxidants	Acetylated Whatman No. 1	Butyl acetate–pyridine–methanol–water (1:5:1:3)		Tollen's reagent Millon's reagent.		108
Basic antioxidants	Schleicher and Schüll 2043b/45ac	96% Ethanol–benzene (1:1)		1% Diazobenzene sulphonic acid (DBS) in 25% aqueous acetic acid or 20 mg. of DBS in 5 ml of 0·1 M NaOH + 5 ml of 96% ethanol		114
Phenolic antioxidants	Schleicher and Schüll 2043b/45ac	Butyl acetate–pyridine–methanol–water (1:5:1:3)		Tollen's reagent, Millon's reagent, phosphomolybdic acid, vanillin or potassium ferricyanide		

TABLE 33. PAPER CHROMATOGRAPHIC SEPARATION OF AMINE ANTIOXIDANTS ACCORDING TO ZIJP[107,111]

Acetylated paper. Mobile phase, benzene:methanol 1:1.
Spray reagent 4% benzoyl peroxide in benzene.

Systematic name	Trade name	Colour of reaction product	Identification limits in micrograms before/after chromatogr. separation		R_f values
1. Phenyl-α-naph-thylamine	Neozone A Nonox A Alterungsschutz-mittel P.A.N.	Light yellow	5	10	0·64
2. Phenyl-β-naph-thylamine	Neozone D Nonox D Alterungsschutz-mittel P.B.N.	Blue-grey	5	20	0·64
3. Diphenyl-p-phenylenedia-mine	J.Z.F.	Yellow-orange	< 1	2	0·56
4. Phenyl-cyclohexyl-p-phenylenedia-mine	Alterungsschutz-mittel 4010	Yellow	< 1	10	0·73
5. Di-β-naphthyl-p-phenylene-diamine	Agerite White Santowhite C.I. Nonox C.I. Alterungsschutz-mittel D.N.P. Antioxidant 123	Pink	1	5	0·55 (Tailing)
6. p-Isoprop-oxydiphenyl-amine	e.g. in Agerite Hipar, a mix-ture of 2, 3 and 6	Yellow-brown	—	—	0·73
7. p,p'-Dimethoxy-diphenylamine	e.g. in Thermoflex A, a mixture of 2, 3 and 7	Brown-pink	—	—	0·68
8. p-(p-Tolyl-sul-phonylamino)-diphenylamine	Aranox	Brown-red	< 1	5	0·65
9. p-(p-Tolyl-sul-phonylamino)-phenyl-p-tolyl-amine	M.U.F.	Red	1	5	0·65
10. Mono- and dihep-tyldiphenyl-amine	Agerite Stalite	Green	—	—	0·81; 0·91
11. 2,4-Diamino-diphenylamine	Oxynone	Brown	< 1	10	0·38
12. p,p'-Diaminodi-phenylmethane	Tonox	Red-brown	2	40	0·50
13. Diphenyl-ethylenediamine	Stabilite	Red-brown	10	80	0·65
14. Di-o-tolyl-ethylene-diamine	Stabilite Alba	Red-brown	10	80	0·67

Whatman No. 1 paper was used for separation. A combination of methods was used to locate the separated antioxidants on the chromatogram. The chromatogram was first examined under ultraviolet radiation, when the compounds were detected either by their intense fluorescence or by absorption when they appeared as dark spots on the paper. The

TABLE 34. PAPER CHROMATOGRAPHIC SEPARATION OF PHENOLIC ANTIOXIDANTS ACCORDING TO ZIJP[107, 111]

Acetylated paper.
Mobile phase.
(1) Butyl acetate–pyridine–methanol–water 1:5:1:3.
(2) Isopropanol–methanol–water 3:3:3.
Spray reagents:
(1) Tollen's reagent.
(2) Millon's reagent.

Systematic name	Trade name	Identification in micrograms before/after chromatogr. separation (Tollen's reagent)	R_f values	
			Mobile phase 1	Mobile phase 2
2,6-Di-tert-butyl-4-methyl phenol	Ionol Deenax	10 / 80	0·60	0·44
2,2'-Methylene-bis-(4-methyl-6-tert-butyl phenol)	2246	1 / 10	0·66	0·55
2,5-Di-tert-amyl-hydroquinone	Santovar A	1 / 40	0·69	0·53 T
2,5-Di-tert-butyl-hydroquinone	Santovar O	1 / 10	0·71	0·55 T
Hydroquinone-mono-benzylether	Agerite Alba	10 / 10	0·66	0·28 T
4,4'-Dihydroxybi-phenyl	Alternungsschutz-mittel D.O.D.	1 / 2	0·77	0·43 T
4,4'-Thio-bis-(6-tert-butyl-3-methyl phenol)	Santowhite Crystals	10 / 40	0·71	0·63 T
4,4'-Thio-bis-(2,5-di-tert-amyl phenol)	Santowhite L	10 / 40	0·58	0·70 T
4,4'-Butylidene-bis (6-tert-butyl-3-methyl phenol)	Santowhite Powder	10 / 40	0·69	0·73 T

T means tailing of the spot.

chromatogram was then sprayed with a 0·05% solution of p-nitrobenzenediazonium fluoborate in acetone to reveal those spots which formed azo dyes.[138] It was possible to detect as little as 2 μg of each antioxidant, and in some cases even less than 1 μg is detected.

The use of acetone as a location reagent solvent is advantageous, since it evaporates off the paper very quickly, thus a chromatogram is not wetted and is easy to handle.

Other reagents were tried by Delves[137] as follows:

(a) A solution of bromine in carbon tetrachloride was found to detect phenothiazine as a blue-grey spot, 3,7-dioctylphenothiazine as a red-brown spot, and di-2-pyridylamine as a transient orange spot.

(b) If the antioxidant solutions were spotted directly on to an untreated paper, and then sprayed with a solution of tetracyanoethylene in benzene,[139] coloured spots were formed similar to the azo dyes obtained with *p*-nitrobenzenediazonium fluoborate. However, after solvent development of the anti-oxidants on paper impregnated with dipropylene glycol, only phenothiazine was detected as a blue-green spot when sprayed with tetracyanoethylene reagent.

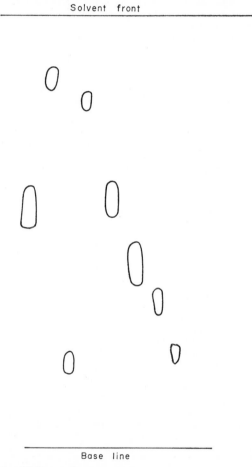

FIG. 37. Paper chromatography of nitrogen containing anti-oxidants. Separated antioxidants visualised with *p*-nitro-benzene diazonium fluoride, Delves[137]. Reproduced by kind permission of the Institute of Petroleum[137].

The R_f values of the antioxidants and the effects observed under ultraviolet radiation and on spraying with *p*-nitrobenzenediazonium fluoborate are given in Table 35.

3.3   The Powerful Combination—Thin-layer Chromatography and Spectroscopy

The identification of mixtures of unknown additives in solvent extracts of polymers presents some difficult problems. The solvent extract is usually available in only fairly small quantities, often consists of a complex mixture requiring preliminary separation into pure components before identifications can be attempted, and is frequently a mixture of compounds of completely unknown type.

Thin-layer chromatography using plates coated with 250 μ adsorbent is an excellent technique for efficiently separating quantities up to 20 mg of total additive mixtures into their individual components. This technique provides a few milligrams of each component, sufficient to prepare a recognizable infrared or ultraviolet and mass spectra which can be compared with the spectra of authentic known compounds. However, the technique does not conveniently handle larger quantities, although preparative thin-layer chromatography using thicker coatings will achieve larger scale separations with some loss of resolution.

TABLE 35. THE PAPER CHROMATOGRAPHIC DETECTION AND IDENTIFICATION OF NITROGEN CONTAINING ANTIOXIDANTS

Antioxidant	Observation under ultra-violet radiation	Colour of azo dye	R_f values (23° C)
Diphenylamine	Nil	Orange-red	0·55
Di-(p-octylphenyl)amine	Absorbs	Yellow	0·86
Phenothiazine	Fluoresces*	Pink	0·19
3,7-Dioctylphenothiazine	Absorbs	Brown-yellow	0·82
N-phenyl-α-naphthylamine	Fluoresces	Mauve	0·57
N-phenyl-β-naphthylamine	Fluoresces	Mauve	0·43
Di-2-naphthylamine	Fluoresces	Mauve	0·34
Di-2-pyridylamine	Fluoresces	Nil	0·22

* At low concentrations phenothiazine is best detected as a dark spot against a white paper background.
Paper chromatograms of the pure antioxidants are shown in Fig. 37.

Numerous works have been published on the experimental technique of thin-layer chromatography which will not be discussed further except in so far as is relevant to its application to additive identification. Dohmann[160] carried out an excellent short review of current techniques. He discusses thin-layer chromatography in the normal sense of the word, i.e. with plate layers up to 250 μ thick and 20 cm × 20 cm or 20 cm × 8 cm in area and also discusses preparative layer chromatography which, with some loss in resolution, can separate considerably larger quantities of compounds on plate layers up to 2 mm thick and 100 cm × 20 cm in area.

Table 36 illustrates the differences in scale of operations between normal analytical thin-layer chromatography, preparative layer chromatography and preparative column chromatography. Separations which have been successfully achieved by analytical thin-layer chromatography may be transferred directly to the preparative layer, because the same sorption media with the same grain size are used in each technique. However, it is not alway possible to transfer directly separations which have been successfully achieved by analytical thin-layer chromatography to preparative column chromatography with equal success because appreciably different adsorbent grain sizes are used in the two techniques.

Halpaap[162] discussed in some detail the experimental technique of preparative scale layer chromatography with sample quantities between 0·1 and 100 g on plates up to 100 cm × 20 cm in area and adsorbent layers up to 2 mm thick.

Stahl[161] has also discussed the general experimental technique of preparative layer chromatography using plates 40 cm × 20 cm in area with up to 1 mm thick coatings. He confirmed that when layer thicknesses are increased appreciably above 250–500 μ, a loss in resolution of separated compounds occurs, although this is not so important when the substances to be separated have a sufficiently large difference in R_f value in the range 0·3–

TABLE 36. COMPARISON OF LAYER AND COLUMN CHROMATOGRAPHY

	Analytical TLC	Preparative layer chromatography (laboratory scale)	Preparative column chromatography (laboratory scale)
Quantity of substance mixture applied	several micrograms	0·1–50 g	1–250 g
Average grain size of adsorbent (silica gel)	5–25 μ	5–25 μ	50–500 μ
Quality of solvent required	10–100 ml	2–5 l	5–100 l
Purity of substances	high purity	high purity only small inter-mixed zones	less purity larger inter-mixed zones
Duration of development	less than 1 hr	less than 1 day	1 to several days

0·8. In these particular circumstances the advantages are combined of achieving good separation with larger sample sizes. However, for the separation of substances which differ in R_f value by 0·2 or less, layer thickness should be limited to maximum of 250 μ with consequent limitations on maximum sample size. In fact, in problems concerned with the identification of additives in polymers, the total quantity of polymer extract sample available for analysis will be rather small, typically 10–100 mg, and in the author's experience, in most instances, true thin-layer chromatography using 250 μ thick layers is admirably suited for the separation of small quantities of the order of 0·1 to 2 mg with excellent resolution. Consequently in this section attention is mainly focused on this technique involving thin-layers of adsorbent up to 250 μ.

Seldom, is sufficient sample available to justify the use of preparative layer chromatography.

Thin-layer Chromatography on 250 μ Thick Layers

Preparation of Solvent Extract of Polymer

Polymer extraction procedures using organic solvents do not extract all types of organic additives from polymers; also many inorganic compounds and metallo-organic compounds (e.g. calcium stearate) are insoluble. The presence of metals will have been indicated in the preliminary examination of the polymer. Most types of organic polymer additives, however, can be readily extracted from polymers with organic solvents of various types.

The first step is to solvent-extract the total additives from the polymer in high yield and with minimum contamination by low molecular polymer. Extracts should be used for analysis without delay as they may contain light- or oxygen-sensitive compounds. When delay is unavoidable, storage in actinic glassware under nitrogen in a refrigerator minimizes the risk of decomposition.

Additives coated on to the surface of a polymer (e.g. antistatic additives) can be removed easily by washing with a low-boiling solvent which does not attack the polymer. These extracts can be concentrated *in vacuo* at 35–40° prior to further analysis. Total internal plus external additives can be extracted from low and high density polyethylene and polystyrene by procedures involving solution or dispersion of the polymer powder or granules (3 g) in cold redistilled sulphur-free toluene (50–100 ml), followed in the case of polyethylene by refluxing for several hours. Rubber-modified polystyrene does not completely dissolve in toluene if it contains gel. Methyl ethyl ketone or propylene oxide are alternative suitable solvents for polystyrene. Dissolved polymer is then reprecipitated by the addition of methyl alcohol or absolute ethanol (up to 300 ml), and polymer removed by filtration or centrifuging. The additive-containing extract can then be concentrated to dryness as described previously. Alternative procedures for the extraction of polyethylene and polypropylene involve refluxing with chloroform for 6 hr or contacting with cold diethyl ether for 24 hr or Soxhlet extraction with diethyl ether, methylene dichloride, chloroform or carbon tetrachloride for 6–24 hr followed by concentration of the extract. Methylene dichloride is a particularly good solvent for polypropylene extractions because of its high volatility and also its small extraction of atatic material from the polymer, compared with other solvents. In addition to additives, most solvents also extract some low molecular weight polymer with subsequent contamination of the extract. To overcome this, Slonaker and Sievers[163] have described a procedure for obtaining polymer-free additive extracts from polyethylene based on low temperature extraction with n-hexane at 0°. This procedure is also applicable to polypropylene and polystyrene.

The possible complications in additive identification that can arise in thin-layer chromatography due to additive degradation by light, heat or oxygen during solvent extraction operations have been well illustrated in the case of the phenolic antioxidant Ionox 330 (1,3,5-trimethyl-2,4,6-tri-(3,5-di-t-butyl-4-hydroxy benzyl) benzene). When 10 μl of a 1% methanol solution of this compound was applied immediately after the solution had been prepared at the base of a silica gel coated plate and the chromatogram then developed by elution with 4:1 cyclohexane:benzene and then a suitable spray reagent applied it was found that only one spot, due to undegraded Ionox 330, appeared part way up the plate. When, however, a 1% methanolic solution of Ionox 330 which had been allowed to stand in air for 10 days was chromatographed under the same conditions it was found that two compounds were present, Ionox 330 and also a degradation product of Ionox 330 which remained unmigrated at the baseline on the chromatogram. Approximately 50% of the

Ionox 330 had degraded during the 10-day standing period, presumably due to oxidation by air possibly assisted by the ultraviolet component of daylight.

Preparation of Thin-layer Plates for Analysis

Plates (20 cm × 20 cm) coated with 250 μ thickness of Merck silica gel G 254 or GF 254 (ultraviolet fluorescent) are suitable for the separation of polymer additives. These plates can either be prepared in the laboratory using an adjustable spreader or, prepared plates can be obtained commercially.†

The glass used to prepare plates should be cleaned with chromic acid, then with deionized water, avoiding detergents, and dried in an air oven prior to coating with silica gel in a clean laboratory atmosphere; conditioning in an air oven for 30 min at 120°C in a vertical position should be followed by storage in a desiccant box until required for use (Fig. 38).[161] The plates should preferably be used within 1–2 hr of preparation so that their activity does not change appreciably and to reduce the possibility of contamination of the silica gel layer by volatile impurities in the laboratory atmosphere which might interfere in the subsequent evaluation of the plates.

Thin-layer chromatographic grades of silica gel usually contain traces of organic impurities. If, during development of a chromatogram, these impurities migrate to regions of the plate which coincide with the R_f values of separated additives, then the impurities will interfere in the interpretation of the plate following spraying with aggressive detection reagents, such as concentrated sulphuric acid and antimony pentachloride, as the organic impurities in the adsorbent also react with these reagents and show up on the sprayed chromatograms. Also, the impurities absorb strongly in the ultraviolet region, especially below 250 mμ. The adsorbent impurities do not have an appreciable adsorption in the infrared region. Thus concentrated chloroform or carbon disulphide extracts of silica gel G have a negligible adsorption over the whole infrared region. As these impurities are extracted from the silica gel with organic solvents such as diethyl ether, ethanol, acetone, benzene, chloroform and many others, they could occur as contaminants in some of the fractions of separated additives isolated from the plate by solvent extraction of the gel and consequently interfere in the interpretation of the spectra of the additives, particularly in the case of additives which absorb below 250 mμ in the ultraviolet. For this reason an identical blank chromatogram (only sample absent) should always be run in parallel with the sample chromatogram in order to check whether such interference effects exist.

It has been shown that the ultraviolet absorbing impurities in adsorbents are influenced by the nature of the migration solvent. Depending on the polarity of the migration solvent used, the impurities migrate to a greater or lesser extent up the plate towards the solvent front with the result that the lower part of the chromatogram nearer the baseline is cleared of impurities, and the impurities become concentrated in the upper section of the plate nearer the solvent front. Subsequently, when a section of the absorbent is removed and eluted with a further solvent to recover a separated compound the amount of impurities contaminating the compound will depend on the location of the compound on the chromatogram (R_f value) and contamination may range from negligible to substantial. The extent to which this redistribution of impurity occurs will be influenced by a number of factors, including the type of absorbent, the particular impurities present, and the migration solvent used. In circumstances where slow moving compounds are being separated, the impurities may move away from the polymer additives towards the solvent front and thus not interfere

† British agents, Anderman & Co. Ltd., Battlebridge House, 87–95 Tooley Street, London, S.E.1.

Fig. 38. Perspex vacuum-desiccator with dry-rack for 10 plates 40×20 cm. Reproduced by kind permission of the Editor of *Laboratory Practice*.[161]

FIG. 39. Developing chamber with rack containing numerous plates, size 40 × 20 cm. The tube in the lid (*front right*) serves for introducing the solvent. Reproduced by kind permission of the Editor of *Laboratory Practice*.[161]

FIG. 40. Automatic applicator for spraying a regular band of sample on plates up to 40 cm wide. Reproduced by kind permission of the Editor of *Laboratory Practice*.[161]

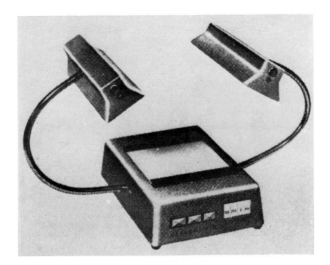

FIG. 41. Uvis-lamp. Two short- and two long-wave ultraviolet tubes are situated in the movable reflectors and may be selectively switched on. For viewing in transmitted light three daylight tubes are seated beneath the clouded-glass screen. Reproduced by kind permission of the Editor of *Laboratory Practice*.[161]

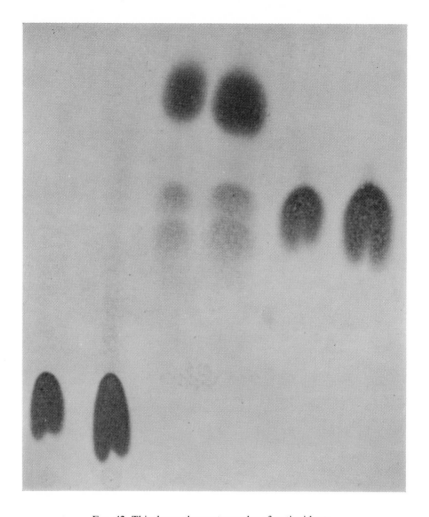

FIG. 42. Thin-layer chromatography of antioxidants.
Three phenolic antioxidants developed with 2:6-dichlorobenzoquinone
chlorimine spray reagent.

in the subsequent examination of the separated compounds. This behaviour leads to a convenient method, described below, for moving the impurities beyond the section of the chromatogram to be used for the separation of polymer additives by migrating the chromatogram with appropriate washing solvents before applying and migrating the sample mixture. If this premigration washing covers a longer distance on the plate than is to be used in the sample migration, then it is possible to move interfering impurities out of the way.

The following procedure has been found to be particularly suitable for the premigration of adsorbent impurities from thin-layer plates prior to the use of the plates for separations of polymer additives. In the case of silica gel, at least, methyl alcohol is the recommended solvent and is much superior to n-hexane. Methanol is poured into a glass tank with a ground glass lid (Fig. 39)[161] to a depth of 1–2 cm and the walls of the tank are lined with sheets of filter paper dipping into the solvent The tank is left for 30–60 min in a draught-free area until the interior has become saturated with solvent vapour. The coated 20 cm × 20 cm plate is then supported vertically in the methanol layer and left until solvent has ascended to the top of the plate (presaturation of the tank facilitates the development of migratory matter in a straight line and speeds up the chromatographic process). The plate is then removed from the tank, conditioned at 120° for 30 min and the top 5–10 cm of adsorbent containing the impurities scraped off with a sharp instrument and thrown away leaving the remainder of the adsorbent coating free from impurities. A second solvent treatment of the plate can be carried out, but is rarely needed. Plates should be used as soon as possible after activation; if a delay is inevitable, then they should be stored in a desiccant box[161] containing silica gel (Fig. 38).

Plates prepared in this way are virtually free from ultraviolet and infrared absorbing impurities and may be used with confidence for interference-free separations of polymer additives.

Premigrated plates should always be reactivated by heating for 30 min at 120°C immediately prior to use in the chromatography of polymer extracts.

Ultraviolet fluorescent grades of silica gel absorbent, discussed later, usually contain manganese activated zinc silicate as a fluorescing agent, e.g. Merck GF 254, Merck G and Camag silica gel G (SG–05F). It has been shown that this compound is not extracted from the adsorbent in the methanol premigration procedure.

Kirchner et al.[164] and Stanley et al.[135] used descending solvent migration from the top edge to the bottom edge of the plates, for removal of adsorbent impurities. This provided effective adsorbent cleaning with little attention. The solvent and migrating impurities are continually removed from the lower edge of the chromatogram and the process continued indefinitely. This method is recommended when substantial numbers of chromatoplates are to be used because it is effective and needs little attention.

Brown and Benjamin[193] have suggested a similar technique in which the direction of washing is across the chromatogram. Their description is sketchy, but apparently solvent flow is maintained across the chromatogram and off the edge as their photographs of developed chromatograms show no concentrated impurity zone along the edge.

Application of Polymer Extract to Plate

Regular application of the sample is particularly important for successful separations. For this purpose, "spotting" as a band is not recommended, and manual application using a pipette requires considerable skill. The procedure suggested by Ritter and Meyer[151] obviates these disadvantages. In this procedure the sample is sprayed on to the layer as a band by means of an automated applicator (Fig. 40). With this instrument a band up to 35 cm long can be applied in a short time. The reversing points of the applicator are practically free from hysteresis so that undesired thickening of the band at the ends does not occur.

In order to minimize washing-out of the sprayed solution at high sample volumes the most volatile solvent possible is chosen, e.g. diethyl ether or methylene dichloride. Where appropriate the plate may be warmed beforehand so as to achieve rapid evaporation of the solvent.

A convenient trial sample size of solvent solution of a polymer extract for application as a band on a 250 μ thick 20 cm × 20 cm plate is 1 ml of a 1% solution, i.e. 10 mg. Depending on the type of separation obtained, larger or smaller sample volumes can then be applied as seems necessary. A further approximate guide for polymer extract sample size for a 250 μ thick 20 cm × 20 cm plate is 0·1–1 mg of polymer extract dissolved in 1 ml solvent per gram of gel loading on the plate. These sample sizes can be increased by a factor of approximately 100 (i.e. 10–100 mg) dissolved in a few millilitres of solvent when carrying out preparative layer chromatography on 20 cm × 40 cm plates with gel thicknesses in the range 750–1500 μ.

Selection of Chromatographic Solvent

Finding a chromatographic development or mixture of solvents for the separation of unknown mixture of additives is not always easy. In some cases a complete separation is not obtained with a single solvent or solvent combination but necessitates the preparation of several chromatograms using different solvents.

An unknown mixture should be first chromatographed on 20 cm × 5 cm plates with solvents of different polarities to obtain an idea of the types of compounds present in the sample and to reduce the possibility of missing any of the sample components. Solvents of low polarity, such as n-hexane, tetrachloroethylene and carbon tetrachloride, cause polar sample constituents on silica gel to migrate to only a small extent but will cause the less polar sample constituents to migrate more readily. Solvents of intermediate polarity such as toluene, benzene, chloroform and methyl cellosolve have a greater elutive effect on polar sample components, whereas highly polar solvents such as dioxan, methylene dichloride, ethyl acetate, nitromethane, acetone, lower alcohols and water elute polar sample constituents towards the solvent front, i.e. R_f values near unity. Mixtures of 40/60 petroleum spirit and up to 10% (v/v) ethyl acetate are very useful general solvents for the separation of unknown mixtures.

Seher[165] has discussed the application of two-dimensional thin-layer chromatography on silica gel to the separation of antioxidants, using development with chloroform in one direction and benzene in the other, and claims separations superior to those obtained in single dimensional chromatography with either of these solvents. Van der Heide *et al.*[166] have described a range of neutral, acidic and basic solvents for the separation of the types of compounds used as additives in polymers. Van der Neut and Maagdenberg[167] describe a scheme for the separation of antioxidants in which they first chromatogram the mixture with a particular solvent and thereby separate the antioxidants into groups according to R_f ranges. Based on this preliminary classification, a second solvent system is selected and then, if necessary, a third and fourth until complete identification is achieved. In all, nine solvent systems are specified together with four detecting reagents. The scheme has been applied, with success, to over thirty antioxidants. New antioxidants can be easily inserted into the scheme. However, the success of this system depends to a large extent on the

TABLE 37. SEPARATION OF ANTIOXIDANTS—THIN-LAYER CHROMATOGRAPHIC METHODS[22]

Substances separated	Stationary phase	Mobile phase	Detection	Refs.
Phenolic antioxidants	Silica Gel G	Methanol–cyclo-hexane (1:24)	30% Molybdophos-phoric acid + ammonia vapour	24
Organo-tin stabilizers	Not stated	Acetic acid–isopropyl ether (1·5:98·5)	20% Molybdophos-phoric acid + ammonia vapour	168
Antioxidants	Not stated	Light petroleum–ethyl acetate (9:1)	(a) Ethanolic 2,6-dichloro-p-benzo-quinone-4-chlor-amine + 2% aq.$Na_2B_4O_7$ (b) Diatzotized p-nitroaniline	25
Organic stabilizers	Kieselgel G	Ethanol-free chloroform		169
Phenolic antioxidants	Polyamide powder	Methanol–water (3:2) or Methanol–carbon tetrachloride (1:9)	Diazotized sulphanilic acid	170
Phenyl sali-cylate Resorcinol benzoate	Kieselgel G	Dichloromethane or isopropyl ether–light petroleum (40–60°) (7:3)	Ultraviolet light	37
BHA,2,6-di-t-butyl-p-cresol	Silica gel	Chloroform	20% Molybdophos-phoric acid + ammonia vapour	171
Antioxidants	Polyamide powder	Methanol–acetone–water (6:1:3)	Diazotized sulph-anilic acid or molybdophosphoric acid	172
Antioxidants	Kieselgel G		α,α'-Diphenyl-β-picryl hydrazyl (free radical)	28
Antioxidants	Alumina + 5% Plaster of Paris on microscope slide	Petrol–dioxane (10:1)	5% Ethanol, phos-phomolybdic acid	175
Antioxidants	Silica gel	Acetone, chloroform, benzene, carbon tetrachloride or binary mixtures		39
Antioxidants	(a) 10% starch in polyamide powder (b) 10% PVC in polyamide	Methanol–acetone–water (3:1:1) light petroleum–benzene–acetic acid–DMF (40:40:20:1)		166
Antioxidants	Silica Gel G	Benzene	0·5% $Fe_2(SO_4)_3$ in sulphuric acid + 0·2% $K_4Fe(CN)_6$ (1:1)	174

reproducibility of the R_f values obtained, and the authors do not, unfortunately, give any account of their experimental procedure. Various solvent systems which have been referred to in the literature[22] for the separation of polymer additives on thin-layer plates are referred to in Table 37.

Detection of Separated Compounds on the Plate

Detection techniques should be carried out immediately after the chromatogram has been developed, in order to reduce to an absolute minimum any opportunity for volatile sample constituents to be lost by evaporation from the plate. Detection of the separated compounds on the plate is achieved by examination under ultraviolet light which locates some, but not all, types of compounds, and by spraying with a range of general or specific spray reagents. Merck GF 254 silica gel contains an inorganic fluorescing additive which is not extracted in the methanol pretreatment discussed previously. Silica gel is suitable for most types of separations. Alumina and cellulose powders are both available in fluorescent forms, respectively, alumina Fluka type D5F, MN cellulose powder 300 F254 (Macherey Nagel & Co.). Exposure of plates to 254 mμ radiation permits visualization of substances on the plate which absorb above 230 mμ as a dark area on a blue fluorescent background. Fluorescent indicators which are activated by long-wavelength ultraviolet light may also be incorporated in the adsorbent. The sodium salts of hydroxypyrene–sulphonic acids are particularly suited for this purpose. The separated polymer constituents show on the chromatogram, partly as dark zones, partly as zones which fluoresce brightly. The Merck silica gel HF 254 + 366 contains two fluorescence indicators, long and short ultraviolet light sensitive. To incite fluorescence, apparatus is needed which will allow a choice of short or long wave ultraviolet radiation. The Desaga-Uvis lamp[161] (Fig. 41) is well suited to this purpose. The non-fluorescent silica gel, Merck G254, reveals the presence of polymer constituents which have an intrinsic fluorescence under short wave (254 mμ) or long wave (366 mμ) ultraviolet light.

To locate separate compounds on the plate with a minimum risk of missing any sample constituents, apply 1 ml of a 1% solution of the polymer extract in a low-boiling solvent such as diethyl ether or methylene dichloride as a continuous band along the base line of each of two 20 cm × 20 cm plates coated with GF 254 and G 254 silica gel, allow the solvent to evaporate, develop the chromatograms and examine the resulting plate under 254 and 366 mμ ultraviolet light sources. After marking off the position of any compounds seen with a stylus, spray the plates with the general spray reagents shown in Table 38, to reveal the presence of any compounds which were not visible under ultraviolet light.

A further general test for organic compounds on the plate involves holding an electrically heated 25 cm long copper wire, set at red heat, at a few millimetres above the plate along the length in which the chromatogram has been developed. After a few seconds exposure, many types of organic compounds reveal themselves by charring or otherwise discolouring.

Further information on the nature of some particular classes of additives can then be obtained by spraying fresh plates with more specific chromogenic reagents (Table 39).

In Fig. 42 is reproduced a typical thin-layer chromatogram obtained for three phenolic antioxidants following spraying with a 1% ethanolic solution of 2,6-dichloro-benzoquinone chlorimine.

The reproducibility of R_f values obtained on chromatoplates is generally poorer than in paper chromatography. Nevertheless, work by Dallas[189] and others[190, 191] have shown that

FIG. 43. Direct transference of the sample-zones into an extraction thimble with the aid of a micro vacuum-cleaner (Ritter and Meyer, 1962). Reproduced by kind permission of the Editor of *Laboratory Practice*.[161]

reproducibility can be distinctly improved if full account is taken of all experimental variables.

TABLE 38. GENERAL SPRAY REAGENTS FOR LOCATION OF COMPOUNDS ON 20 CM × 20 CM SILICA GEL COATED THIN-LAYER CHROMATOGRAPHY PLATES

A. Reagents applied to GF 254 plate without subsequent heating*

(i)	Potassium permanganate	(0·1 N) in aqueous sodium carbonate (5% w/v)
(ii)	Potassium permanganate	(2% w/v) in aqueous sulphuric acid (6% v/v)
(iii)	Potassium permanganate	(0·1% w/v) in sulphuric acid (96%)
(iv)	Antimony pentachloride	(2% w/v) in carbon tetrachloride
(v)	Phosphomolybdic acid	(3% w/v) in ethanol, then expose plate to ammonia vapour

B. Reagents applied to G 254 plate with subsequent heating*

		Heat treatment of plate
(i)	Sulphuric acid aqueous (20% w/v)	5–15 min at 120°C, then 5 min at 150°C
(ii)	As (ii) under A	5–15 min at 120°C, then 5 min at 150°C
(iii)	Phosphoric acid (10%) methanolic	5–15 min at 120°C, then 5 min at 150°C
(iv)	Perchloric acid (2%) methanolic	5–15 min at 120°C, then 5 min at 150°C
(v)	As (iv) under A	5–15 min at 120°C, then 5 min at 150°C
(vi)	Phosphomolybdic acid (20% w/v) in methanol or methyl cellosolve, then expose plate to ammonia vapour	5–15 min at 120°C

* Spray 20 cm × 2 cm wide sections of plate with each reagent using an aluminium or glass mask with suitable aperture.

Removal of Separated Compounds from Plate

Examination of the plates under ultraviolet light and by the application of general and specific spray reagents as described in the previous section will usually provide full information regarding the R_f values in different development solvents of the various components of the original additive mixture applied to the plate and, possibly some information regarding the types of compounds present.

It is emphasized here that in order to avoid "missing" any sample components it is highly advisable to apply the sample location techniques described in the last section to chromatograms of the sample obtained using several plate materials such as silica gels and alumina, and with each adsorbent to use as wide a variety as possible of different types of development solvents. These steps reduce to a minimum mistakes brought about by supposedly pure separated compounds consisting, in fact, of two or more unresolved compounds and enable a suitable development solvent to be selected. Application of a wide range of detection methods reduces to a minimum the chance of not observing any of the separated compounds. Having full information on the R_f values of the different sample components

TABLE 39. SPECIFIC SPRAY REAGENTS FOR LOCATION OF COMPOUNDS BY THIN-LAYER CHROMATOGRAPHY

Additive type	Spray reagent	Ref.
Phenolic antioxidants	(i) 2,6-dichloro-benzoquinone chlorimine (1–2% in ethanol followed 15 min later by 2% borax in 40% aqueous ethanol).	176, 177, 178, 179
	(ii) αα'-diphenyl picryl hydrazyl (0·1% in 95% aqueous ethanol).	179
	(iii) Palladium chloride. (Mix 150 ml palladium chloride with 100 ml of 2 N hydrochloric acid.)	179
	(iv) Diazotized p-nitroaniline. (Mix 5 ml 0·5% p-nitroaniline in 2 N hydrochloric acid with 0·5 ml 5% sodium nitrite until colourless and 15 min later add 15 ml 20% sodium acetate.)	178
Amine antioxidants	Diazotized p-nitroaniline. (Mix 5 ml 0·5% p-nitroaniline in 2 N hydrochloric acid with 0·5 ml 5% sodium nitrite, until colourless and 15 min later add 15 ml 20% sodium acetate.)	
Dialkyl thiodipropionates	Potassium platinoiodide. (Mix 5 ml 5% platinum tetrachloride in 1 N hydrochloric acid with 45 ml 10% potassium iodide and 100 ml water.)	179
Phthalate ester plasticizers	Resorcinol. (Spray with 20% aqueous resorcinol in 2% aqueous zinc chloride and heat to 150°. Then spray with 4 N sulphuric acid and heat for 20 min at 120°. Spray with 40% potassium hydroxide to produce orange spots.) Phthalic acid and phthalates also react.	180, 181
Acids and bases	Bromocresol green ⎫	182, 186
	Bromocresol purple ⎬ (0·5% in 50% aqueous	182, 183
	Bromophenol blue ⎭ ethanol).	182
	Methyl red	182, 184
Carboxylic acids	Sodium dichlorophenolindophenol (1% ethanolic).	182
Aliphatic (primary, secondary and tertiary) amines, long chain quaternary salts and amine oxides	Cobalt thiocyanate 10 g Co(NO₃)₂6H₂O and 10 g ammonium thiocyanate made up to 100 ml. Produces blue colour.	185
Alkanolamines	Ninhydrin. (Heat plate for 5 min at 110°, spray with 0·2% ninhydrin in acetone and heat 5 min at 110° to produce colours. Further colours then produced upon spraying plate with 0·2% alizarin in acetone.)	
Alkyl phenols	Phenols coupled as p-nitrophenol azo dyes applied to plate of silica gel impregnated with alkali. Separated azo dyes located as yellow/red colours upon exposure of plate to ammonia vapour.	187
Carbonyl compounds	Carbonyl compounds in sample converted to 2,4-dinitrophenylhydrazones, applied to thin-layer plate and plate developed. Separated 24 DNPH compounds located as yellow or brown colours upon spraying plate with 2% sodium hydroxide in 90% ethanol.	188
Organic peroxides	Hydriodic acid. (Spray plate with a reagent comprising 40 ml glacial acetic acid and 0·2 g zinc dust added to 10 ml of 4% aq. potassium iodide, then spray with fresh 1% starch solution.) Peroxides (and certain other types of oxidizing agents) revealed by liberation of free iodine.	
	(a) Alternatively use 2,6-dibromo-benzoquinone chlorimine.	

* Spray 20 cm × 2 cm wide sections of the plate with the various reagents using an aluminium or glass mask with suitable aperture.

using the preferred development solvents, the next stage is to run a chromatogram on fresh 20 cm × 20 cm plates using a suitably sized sample (say 1 ml of a 1% solution) and mark off with a sharp stylus the bands corresponding to the known positions of the separated compounds. No detection reagents are applied to these plates although they may be examined under the ultraviolet light to precisely locate any components which show up under these conditions. The simplest method of removing the zones containing the separated compounds (after allowing solvent to evaporate from the plate) is to hold the plate vertically its side resting on a sheet of paper and to scrape off the desired zone with a spatula. For substances which are not sensitive to oxidation, the zones may be sucked from the layer directly into an extraction thimble by using a small "vacuum cleaner"[151, 161] (Fig. 43). Each separated adsorbent band can then be bottled off in 5-ml polythene stoppered tubes and retained for further examination.

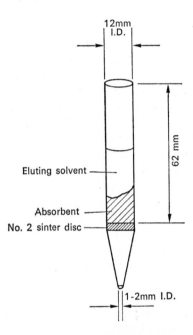

12mm I.D.

62 mm

Eluting solvent

Absorbent

No. 2 sinter disc

1-2mm I.D.

FIG. 44. Filtration apparatus for extracting separated additives from adsorbent. Isolated from thin-layer chromatography plates.

Extraction of Pure Polymer Additives from Separated Adsorbent Bands.

The separated portions of adsorbent, each, hopefully, containing a pure constituent of the original polymer extract, are now extracted with suitable solvents to isolate the additive preparatory to identification by physical and chemical methods.

Each portion of adsorbent is transferred from the storage bottle to a separate small sintered glass extraction thimble (Fig. 44) and the organic compounds leached out with a suitable solvent such as anhydrous absolute ethanol, diethyl ether or methylene dichloride. This solvent must:

(i) be a good solvent for the additive;

(ii) be sufficiently polar to desorb the additive from the adsorbent (successive desorption with different solvents may be necessary at this stage);

(iii) have a low boiling point to facilitate subsequent removal of solvent and reduce to a minimum evaporation losses of any volatile sample constituents; and/or

(iv) not interfere in the subsequent spectroscopic examination of extracts.

Provided the desorption solvent is sufficiently powerful and polar, it should recover between 50 and 100% of the additive present in the silica gel fraction and provide sufficient material for examination by ultraviolet or infrared spectroscopy, or mass spectroscopy.

During the solvent elution of compounds from the isolated bands of adsorbent, the elution solvent effectively displaces the components from the adsorbent so that all of the component is contained in the first liquid emerging from the sintered glass thimble. Loss of the component by its failure to elute is not usually serious, provided that the eluant selected is one which would elute the particular compound to the solvent front (i.e. R_f near unity) on a thin-layer plate. In fact, the behaviour of the component on the plate with plate elution solvents is a good guide to the selection of an appropriate solvent for desorbing the same component from the isolated gel in the extraction thimble. If the elution solvent used is less effective than this, then losses can be expected of the compound at the adsorbent extraction stage.

In extractions from silica gel, care should be taken to ensure that, according to the solvent used, components of the adsorbent are not co-extracted with polymer additives. Silica gel and cellulose powder adsorbents containing gypsum as a binder cannot be extracted with water or with aqueous organic solvent mixtures because calcium sulphate is quantitatively extracted at the same time. Honegger[145] showed that a significant extraction residue is obtained even using chloroform benzene or acetone as extractants. A significant inorganic extraction residue is also obtained from gypsum-free silica gel to which silicon dioxide of particle size less than 40 mμ is added as a binder; this extract decreases with decreasing polarity of the extraction solvent. The extract solution should, therefore, be filtered through a hardened filter at the base of the extraction thimble (Fig. 44), and/or through short columns of Celite. Alternatively, the solvent extract can be evaporated to dryness and the silica contaminated residue contacted with a good solvent for the polymer additive and a bad solvent for the silica.

Polar elution solvents, especially if they contain water, will extract inorganic salts such as calcium sulphate from Silica Gel G; thus 10 ml of 35:65 v/v acetonitrile:water extracted 0.4% of salts from Merck AG Silica Gel G.

Ultraviolet fluorescent type silica gel absorbents contain inorganic additives to induce fluorescence. Thus, Merck AG fluorescent silica gel and Camag Silica Gel G (SG-5DF) are stated to contain manganese-activated zinc silicate. After plates of these adsorbents had been premigrated with methyl alcohol, as described earlier, it was found that solvent extracts of the isolated gel did not absorb in the ultraviolet region between 200 and 300 mμ or in the infrared. Hence, this type of fluorescent activator would not be expected to interfere in the examination of polymer additive extracts obtained from this type of adsorbent.

In Table 40 are summarized the results obtained in some experiments carried out to determine the recovery of compounds absorbing at shorter and longer ultraviolet wavelengths, respectively, di-n-butyl phthalate (222 mμ) and Ionox 330 (277 mμ). These compounds were carried through the whole series of operations involving application of sample to a silica gel plate, solvent development, separation of adsorbent from plate and, finally, solvent extraction of the compound from the adsorbent.

Ionox 330 has a low R_f value with 4:1 cyclohexane:benzene development solvent (Table 40) and hence, during solvent development, ultraviolet absorbing adsorbent impurities are swept well away from this compound to the solvent front. Premigration of the plate with methyl alcohol was unnecessary and not used, therefore, prior to application of Ionox 330 to the plate. Premigration of the plate with methanol before sample application was, however, carried out in the case of di-n-butyl phthalate. This was because this compound has a fairly high R_f value with the 9:1 iso-octane:ethyl acetate development solvent used, with consequent possible contamination of the di-n-butyl phthalate band with ultraviolet absorbing adsorbent impurities near the solvent front. It is seen in Table 40 that satisfactory recoveries of both compounds were obtained by this procedure.

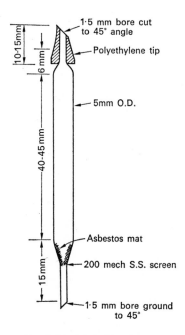

FIG. 45. Collector tube for quantitative removal of sample zone from thin-layer plate.[192]

Millet et al.[192] have discussed in some detail rapid techniques for quantitatively recovering separated substances from thin-layer plates. They use a precision streaking device for applying the original sample to the plate. Following irrigation of the plate with development solvent, the substrate and separated components are picked up in vacuum collector tubes fashioned from sections in 5 mm borosilicate tubing (Fig. 45). By varying the collector tube length and diameter, sample sizes ranging from micro to preparative can be handled. Chromatographic elution of sample from the resulting powder columns isolated in the collector tubes is accomplished through transfer of a solvent from a reservoir by means of a thread wick (Fig. 46). Elution volumes are minimal, 100 μl providing quantitative recovery of a separated component, thus favouring subsequent examination by micro-ultraviolet, infrared and gas chromatographic and other techniques. Using mixtures of furoic and hydroxymethyl furoic acids, Millet *et al.*[192] applied the technique over a range of plate loadings between 1 and 100 μg and demonstrated excellent precision and accuracy in the recoveries obtained in the overall procedure (Table 41).

Preparation of Infrared Spectra of Separated Polymer Additives

A method is described below for preparing infrared spectra of the various portions, each containing a single polymer additive, isolated from the thin-layer plate. Hummel[323] has published a comprehensive table giving infrared spectra of many types of polymer additives.

McCoy[324] has developed a technique for obtaining infrared spectra of from 50 to 100 μg of components isolated from a thin-layer plate. This technique, described below, utilizes an infrared cavity micro-cell.

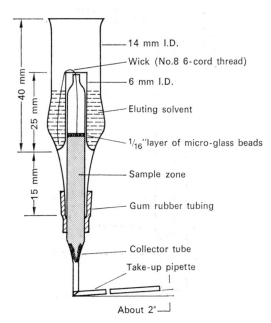

14 mm I.D.

Wick (No.8 6-cord thread)

6 mm I.D.

Eluting solvent

$\frac{1}{16}$" layer of micro-glass beads

Sample zone

Gum rubber tubing

Collector tube

Take-up pipette

About 2°

Fig. 46. Elution assembly for quantitative recovery of adsorbent isolated from thin-layer chromatography plates.[192]

Apparatus

Elution columns, disposable, made from Pasteur-type pipettes as shown in Fig. 47. Pack a glass wool plug firmly into the larger half of the tapered section as shown in Fig. 47. A more retentive pad is obtained if the glass wool pad is dampened with a few drops of the elution solvent to be used just before use. Excess liquid is removed by drawing air through the column.

Evaporation assembly, as shown in Fig. 48.

Infrared spectrophotometer fitted with a beam condenser and "ultramicro" cavity cells.

Centrifuge and accessories.

Micromanipulator, Microchemical Specialties Co., Berkeley, Calif., No. 5020.

(a) Pasteur type disposable pipette (BKH No.53039, 9 inch length)

(b) Pipette modified and ready for elution

(c) Capillary before evaporation

(d) Capillary after evaporation

FIG. 47. Steps in preparation and use of elution column used for GLC fraction collecting.[324] (a) Pasteur-type disposable pipette (BKH No. 53039, 9 in. length); (b) Pipette modified and ready for elution; (c) Capillary before evaporation; (d) Capillary after evaporation.

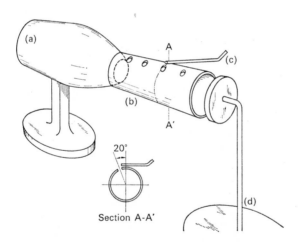

FIG. 48. Apparatus for evaporation of solvent from capillaries. Prior to infrared spectroscopy[324]

(a) Hair dryer.

(b) Metal or glass tube a little larger in diameter than the air outlet of the hair dryer and 6 in. long. Drill four 0·25 in. holes 1 in. apart in a straight line as shown. Mount with holes rotated 20° from the vertical as shown in section A–A'.

(c) Capillary containing liquid to be evaporated. Hold horizontal in a simple micromanipulator such as that sold by Microchemical Specialities Co., Berkeley, Calif., Cat. No. 5020.

(d) Moveable stand holding a solid disc of same diameter as tube which serves as a damper to adjust air flow out the side holes.

TABLE 40. REPRODUCIBILITY OF RECOVERY OF IONOX 330 AND DI-N-BUTYL PHTHALATE FROM THIN-LAYER PLATE (SILICA GEL G254)

Compound	Absorbance maximum	Number of plates prepared	Sample size† μl	Sample concentration %w/v	Development solvent	Plate drying time hr	Section of adsorbent removed from plate R	Solvent used to desorb compound from adsorbent	Absorptivity of standard solution of compound litres g cm	Recovery of compound ¶	Standard deviation
Ionox 330	277 mμ	10	1	1	4:1 cyclo-hexane: benzene	18§	0·03–0·14	Methanol (extract made up 1 ml)	8·0	100	1·2
Di-n-butyl-p-phthalate‡	222 mμ	5	1	5	9:1 iso-octane: ethyl acetate	18	—	Methanol (extract made up to 1 ml)	29·0	99·6	1·2

† Applied by Hamilton PR600 repeating sample dispenser.
‡ Plate premigrated once with methyl alcohol then reconditioned for 1 hr at 120° C before application of sample.
§ To allow complete evaporation of benzene which would interfere in subsequent ultraviolet spectroscopy.
¶ Based on ratio of theoretical absorptivity and absorptivity of extract from thin-layer plate; methanol used in reference cell in all experiments.

TABLE 41. QUANTITATIVE RECOVERY BY THIN-LAYER CHROMATOGRAPHY, RECOVERY OF FUROIC
ACIDS APPLIED AT VARIOUS PLATE LOADING LEVELS

Acid, μg						Mean, μg	Range, μg	Rel. std. dev., %	Rel. error %
Applied	Recovered in Replicate								
Furoic									
99·72	99·50	99·05	99·50	100·65	100·65	99·87	1·60	0·74	+0·15
72·16	71·28	71·00	71·28	72·19	71·74	71·50	1·19	0·66	−0·91
50·52	49·78	50·33	50·42	50·78	50·23	50·31	1·00	0·72	−0·42
25·24	25·62	25·44	25·39	25·53	25·26	25·45	0·36	0·91	+0·83
12·83	12·91	12·76	12·74	12·72	12·45	12·72	0·46	1·31	−0·86
5·96	6·06	6·08	5·99	5·88	5·89	5·88	0·20	1·56	+0·34
Hydroxymethylfuroic									
92·86	89·68	89·43	90·93	90·43	90·93	90·28	1·50	0·77	−2·78
72·57	70·96	71·06	71·27	71·06	70·66	71·00	0·61	0·31	−2·19
47·97	47·05	46·35	46·45	46·85	46·85	46·71	0·70	0·63	−2·63
14·52	14·36	13·75	13·91	13·75	14·06	13·97	0·61	1·83	−3·79
12·27	11·47	11·83	11·66	11·62	11·38	11·59	0·45	1·51	−5·54
6·13	5·52	5·60	5·59	5·77	5·61	5·62	0·25	1·64	−8·32

Procedure

The solvents used for the development of the plate must be volatile enough to be removed from the adsorbent by evaporation and the adsorbent itself must not contain impurities which will show a significant absorbance in the infrared when treated as described below. In general, inorganic adsorbents, such as silica gel or alumina are satisfactory but blank determinations should be made to verify behaviour of each lot of adsorbent with solvents to be used. About 100 μg of a separated component is optimum; smaller amounts will sometimes suffice depending upon how effectively it is eluted and transferred.

ELUTION. Transfer the adsorbent to the elution column (Fig. 47) and pack it firmly and evenly on top of the glass wool pad using a 5-cm glass rod with a square end. The adsorbent when packed into the tube should form a bed from 1·5 to 2 cm thick to minimize chances for "channelling" and so that the flow rate is not too fast. When eluting smaller amounts additional adsorbent should be mixed with that removed from the chromatogram before the column is packed. Mount the column in a vertical position and add a few drops of a solvent that will effectively displace the compound from the adsorbent. A suitable eluting solvent is one which moves the component with an R_f of 1 (at the solvent front) on a thin-layer chromatogram using the same adsorbent. Effective elution is required since only about 0·1 ml of solvent passes through the packed column. Do not allow the capillary to fill beyond the bend as this makes it more difficult to handle the filled capillary. Allow the elution to continue until the capillary section is filled nearly to the bend near the end.

Lay the elution column on its side and scratch the column below the glass wool pad such that the scratch is on the tapered transition section between the capillary and the larger section at a point where the diameter is nearly, but not more than,

3 mm (this end must fit into a $\frac{1}{8}$ in. diameter hole). Hold the capillary section motionless and break the larger section away from the capillary. The scratch is conveniently made with an ampoule file. If the capillary section is held motionless when the column is broken, no liquid will be spilled except a little which is close to the break. This portion is not important as most of the solute will be in the lower section of the capillary. The capillary containing the solution can be handled without spilling the contents by holding it at a slight angle from the horizontal with the bent end low. A convenient way is to place the capillary on the mounting block of the micro-manipulator so the point to be cut is at the end of the block. Clip it down, make the scratch, and break the column by bending over the end of the block. After cutting, slide the capillary so the cut end protrudes about 1·5 in.

EVAPORATION. Mount the capillary in a horizontal position with the bent tip pointing upwards using the micromanipulator to hold it. Position it over the evaporation assembly (Fig. 48) so that the flared end is directly over and about 2 mm above one of the small holes. When doing this, position the liquid in the capillary so that the meniscus is a few millimetres from the flared end. Direct the warm air flow from the hair dryer into the large tube and gradually move the glass stopper which serves as a damper to partially close the other end. Observe the liquid in the capillary carefully, and, as the air flow through the side holes increases, the meniscus will be drawn towards the end. Adjust the air flow until the meniscus is about 2–3 mm from the end. Avoid drawing the meniscus to the end as capillary forces will transfer part of the solution to the outside where it will be lost. Allow the evaporation to proceed. Normally the solvent will evaporate smoothly without further attention except in the last stages; if necessary, the capillary may be tilted a little to maintain the meniscus in the desired position.

RESOLUTION AND TRANSFER. Remove the capillary from the evaporation assembly, hold it in the air stream for a few seconds so any vapour present is flushed out, and inject 5 μl of solvent, usually carbon tetrachloride or carbon disulphide, into the bent end of the capillary. Manipulate the capillary which is held nearly horizontal by tilting and rotating it so that the droplet of solvent moves and contacts the entire inside surface to dissolve the residue Be sure to contact the zone near the flared end where the evaporation occurred as a large part of the residue is deposited at this point. The presence of adsorbent in the capillary at this stage may prevent transfer of the residue to the infrared cell. This can happen when the adsorbent adsorbs the residue so strongly that the solvent used for the transfer does not elute it.

Place an "ultramicro" cavity cell in a plastic centrifuge tube, hold the tube in a horizontal position and insert the flared end of the capillary into the filling hole of the cell. Place the tube in the centrifuge and centrifuge the solution into the cell. Remove the capillary and examine the cell to see if more sample solution is present than is needed to fill the cell. If so, evaporate the excess volume of solvent by drawing a stream of air across the top of the cell. Seal the cell with a drop of mercury.

The infrared spectrum of the solvent solution can then be obtained by normal infrared spectroscopic techniques.

Alternatively, especially if the compound is insoluble in the usual spectroscopic solvents, the solid can be dispersed in well-ground solid dry potassium bromide using a dental mixing machine and the mixture pressed into a 1 mm thick 5 mm diameter disc. This disc can then be mounted in a cardboard or plastic holder and used to prepare a spectrum.

Preparation of Ultraviolet Spectra of Separated Polymer Additives

Apparatus

Elution columns, disposable, made from Pasteur-type pipette (230 mm size) by cutting the larger section about 2 cm below the constriction and shortening the capillary end to about 5 cm in length. Mount in a vertical position (Fig. 47).

Volumetric flasks, 0·5- and 1-ml sizes.

Microspatula, Hayman type, Arthur H. Thomas Co., No. 9007-A, or other similar tool having a sharp, square end suitable for scraping the adsorbent layer from the glass backing.

Ultraviolet spectrophotometric equipment such as the Applied Physics Corp., (Cary) Models Nos. 14 or 15, the Beckman Model DU or others which can be used with the micro cells described below.

Micro cells and accessory equipment. "Rectangular Micro Cells" (Code S-18-120), The Ultracell Co., Emerson, New Jersey. This company supplies a holder and mask for use with the Beckman Model DU. A simple mask as shown in Fig. 49 is needed to use these cells with the Applied Physics Corp., Models Nos. 14 or 15.

After chromatography, the chromatogram is air-dried as necessary to remove residual migration solvent. If ultraviolet transparent solvents have been used that will not interfere with subsequent measurements, only a few minutes are needed to dry the adsorbent enough for the next step. When the solvent itself would interfere subsequently in ultraviolet spectroscopy, thorough removal by evaporation is necessary; several hours may be required. Illuminate the chromatogram with an ultraviolet light (2537 mμ) and mark the locations of the separated compounds which are visible as dark or fluorescing spots on the fluorescent background. Mark areas a little larger than those on which sample can be seen, if possible, to be more certain of including all of the compound. At this stage, compounds that absorb in the visible can be seen directly and need not be exposed to the ultraviolet light.

The amount of sample required for the preparation of a spectrum depends on the absorptivity of the particular compound. 10 μg of a compound having an absorptivity of 10 l/g-cm will give an absorbance reading of 0·1 when dissolved in 1 ml of solvent and measured according to this procedure.

ELUTION. Prepare the necessary number of elution columns (Fig. 47) as follows:

Hold a tuft of glass wool in a pair of tweezers and rinse it with absolute ethanol. While still dripping wet, insert it into the top of a column and pack it into the tapered section with a 2-mm glass rod. Pack firmly. At this stage the capillary in the lower section fills with ethanol displaced from the glass wool; leave the capillary filled at this stage and prepare the rest of the columns needed.

Just before transferring the adsorbent, supported on a piece of creased glazed paper, to the elution column, shake the column to remove the ethanol in the capillary but do not dry the glass wool. Transfer the adsorbent to the column by folding the paper slightly and, while holding the crease at the top of the column, tapping the paper gently. Pack the adsorbent evenly but not too firmly with a 2-mm glass rod. If the glass wool is damp when the dry adsorbent is added it effectively stops any of the dry powder from sifting through the wool. In addition, the adsorbent becomes a little damp and packs more easily. Packing should be firm enough so that from 15 to 30 min are required for 1 ml of elution solvent to pass through. Too firm packing causes the flow rate to be too slow; if this happens, application of moderate air pressure can be used to speed the elution. Some practice in packing and eluting is recommended to learn how to achieve proper packing. The more probable error is in packing too tightly; in handling the rod the maximum force that should be exerted is just about the minimum that can be felt in the fingers holding the rod.

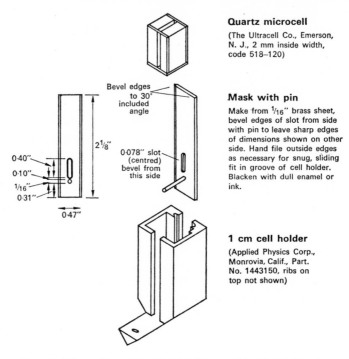

Quartz microcell

(The Ultracell Co., Emerson, N. J., 2 mm inside width, code 518–120)

Bevel edges to 30° included angle

Mask with pin

Make from $1/16''$ brass sheet, bevel edges of slot from side with pin to leave sharp edges of dimensions shown on other side. Hand file outside edges as necessary for snug, sliding fit in groove of cell holder. Blacken with dull enamel or ink.

$2\frac{1}{8}''$

$0.40''$

$0.10''$

$1/16''$

$0.31''$

$0.078''$ slot (centred) bevel from this side

$0.47''$

1 cm cell holder

(Applied Physics Corp., Monrovia, Calif., Part. No. 1443150, ribs on top not shown)

FIG. 49. Microcell, mask, and cell holder used in ultraviolet spectroscopy.

Place a 0·5- or 1-ml volumetric flask beneath the column and add a little elution solvent to the column so that the walls and glass rod are rinsed. Allow all of the liquid to pass into the adsorbent and add a little more. The total volume added should be a little less than is needed to fill the flask and it should be added in about three increments when quantitative recovery is desired. After the liquid has ceased emerging from the column, apply gentle air pressure to empty the capillary, remove the column, and dilute the volumetric flask to the mark. Stopper and mix.

MEASUREMENT. Measure the absorbance of the solution at the desired wavelength or record its spectrum using small volume micro cells. Either air or the elution solvent may be used as the reference. Blank determinations which were carried through the entire procedure, including chromatography, should always be made and measured or recorded. It is important that the sections of adsorbent eluted for the blanks come from chromatograms prepared and handled in the same manner as the sample chromatogram and that they represent the same areas and locations of adsorbent. This is necessary because impurities, if present, are not distributed uniformly on the chromatogram. Removal of impurities from the region of the adsorbent layer to be used for the sample separation by washing the layer prior to migration of the sample using the methanol premigration technique described earlier is a convenient and effective method of reducing blank absorption.

STANDARDS. When quantitative determinations are desired using this technique, it is necessary to know or to determine the absorptivities of the particular compounds. This is done by preparing and measuring solutions of known concentration of the pure compounds. It is also advisable to chromatograph known amounts of the pure compounds to verify the applicability of the technique to the particular compounds. This is recommended because unexpected errors can occur if compounds have enough volatility to escape from the adsorbent or are unstable and change during the chromatography and drying.

Mass spectrometry has been applied by Djerassi et al.[325, 326] to the identification of amine antioxidants and Leblank[327] has described infrared and mass spectrometric techniques for the identification of Ionol in polymers.

Examples of Identification of Additives by Combined Thin-layer Chromatography/Infrared Spectroscopy

The first example concerns three polyolefins suspected to contain one or more of the following additives: Topanol CA (tris(2-methyl-4-hydroxy-5-tert-butyl phenyl), butane), DLTDP (dilauryl thiodipropionate) and Ionox 330 (1,3,5-tri-methyl-2,4,6-tri (3,5-di-tert-butyl-4-hydroxy benzyl) benzene).

Additives were removed from 30 g of each of the polymers by a 6-hr Soxhlet extraction with diethyl ether. The extract residues were made up to 10 ml with chloroform, and 10 μl of these solutions and solutions of authentic specimens of the three additives mentioned above were spotted on to Merck GF 254 silica gel plate and the chromatograms developed using 9:1 (v/v) 40/60 petroleum spirit:ethyl acetate solvent. Viewing the plates under 254 mμ ultraviolet light located Ionox 330 and Topanol CA but not DLTDP. All three additives were, however, located with aggressive spray reagents and with a reagent for phenols (2:6-dibromo-benzoquinone-4-chlorimine, which gives strong colours with hindered phenols and also a yellow colour with DLTDP). The chromatograms in Fig. 50 show that polymers 1 and 2 both contained DLTDP and Ionox 330, polymer 2 also contained Topanol CA, whilst polymer 3 contained DLTDP and Topanol CA. Both of the aggressive spray reagents revealed the presence of low molecular weight polymer at the solvent front (spot vi). These reagents also revealed the presence in the authentic specimen of Topanol CA of an impurity which appears at the solvent front. Obviously, this impurity is of low polarity and is not phenolic as evidenced by the fact that it does not produce a colour with the phenol reagent. It is probably a hydrocarbon.

A further example concerns the identification of an ultraviolet light stabilizer and an antioxidant in a sample of a polyolefin. Again the polymer was extracted with diethyl ether to isolate total additives and a portion of a chloroform solution of the extract and of various known light stabilizers and antioxidants run in parallel on a silica gel coated plate.

The chromatograms in Fig. 51 show that the polymer contained two additives appearing at R_f 0·6 and 0·85 which coincided in R_f value and in the colour obtained with 2,6-dibromo-benzoquinone-4-chlorimine with known specimens of UV 531 (2-hydroxy-4-n-octoxy benzophenone) and Ionol CP (2,6-di-tert-butyl-*p*-cresol). Spraying the plate with 2,6-dibromo-benzoquinone-4-chlorimine also revealed an additional orange coloured spot at R_f 0·8 which did not coincide with any of the known additives examined.

E

Next, an attempt was made to identify unequivocally these three polymer components by comparing their infrared spectra with those of authentic specimens of the suspected compounds. Chloroform solutions (1 ml) containing 15–30 mg of the polymer extract and of authentic UV 531 and Ionol CP were applied along the edge of three 20 cm × 20 cm

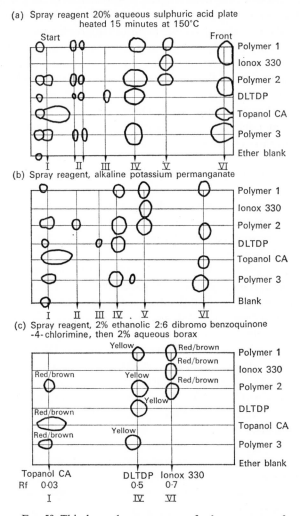

Fig. 50. Thin-layer chromatograms of solvent extracts of three polyolefins. Plate: Merck silica gel GF 254; development solvent: 40/60 petroleum spirit:ethyl acetate (9:1 v/v).

plates and the chromatograms developed using 40/60 petroleum spirit:ethyl acetate (9:1 v/v). The three ultraviolet adsorbing bands on each plate were then marked off and the silica gel corresponding to these zones removed from the plate and the additive extracted from each portion of gel with anhydrous diethyl ether. After removing ether, the residues were intimately mixed with dry potassium bromide and small discs prepared for infrared spectroscopy. As a control a further blank chromatogram was developed, omitting the addition of chloroform solution of sample. The gel from this plate corresponding in R_f value and area to the R_f 0·6 and 0·8/0·85 bands observed in the polymer extract, were isolated and ether extracted. Figures 52 and 53 show the infrared spectra in the 2·5 to 15 μ region of the authentic additives (direct spectrum *a* and spectrum after separation on the plate *b*), the blank run *c* and the corresponding extract of the polymer *d, e*. The spectra *a* and *b* of authentic UV 531 are identical, as are spectra *a* and *b* in the case of Ionol CP, i.e. it is valid to compare the spectra of these additives after chromatography with their direct infrared

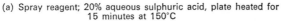

(a) Spray reagent; 20% aqueous sulphuric acid, plate heated for 15 minutes at 150°C

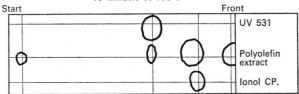

(b) Spray reagent; 2% ethanolic 2:6 dibromo benzoquinone-4-chlorimine; then 2% aqueous borax

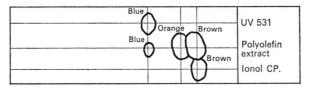

FIG. 51. Thin-layer chromatograms of solvent extracts of polyolefin nibs. Plate: Merck silica gel GF 254, development solvent: 40 : 60 petroleum spirit:ethyl acetate (9 : 1 v/v).

spectra, indicating that contact with silica gel does not produce any structural alteration of these substances. Also, the blank spectra in Figs. 52 and 53 show that only minor infrared absorptions due to plate impurities occur at 6·1 μ (water), and 8–10, 10·5, 13 μ (silica gel) and 7·2 μ (grease from glassware). These absorptions would not interfere in the interpretation of the additives spectra.

Comparison of Figs. 52 *b* and *d* reveals that the compound at R_f 0·6 is identical or very similar to UV 531. The light stabilizer in the polymer extract is certainly a substituted benzophenone, although it may differ from UV 531 in the length of the alkoxy substituent which is known to have little or no influence on the infrared spectrum of compounds of this class.

Comparison of Figs. 53 *b* and *d* confirms that the R_f 0·85 compound in the polymer extract is Ionol CP, and comparison of *d* and *e* shows that the R_f 0·8 component of the polymer extract has a spectrum very similar to that of authentic Ionol CP, suggesting that it is a breakdown product produced, presumably, by partial degradation of Ionol CP during polymer processing.

A further example concerns the identification of additives in a sample of polystyrene. Preliminary thin-layer chromatography on silica gel of an extract of the polymer revealed the presence of four additives with R_f values of 0·0, 0·45, 0·8 and 0·9. Obviously, the substance that had not migrated has a high affinity for silica gel and, in fact, a very polar solvent combination (1:1 v/v chloroform:ethanol) was needed to desorb this compound. The other three less polar compounds were easily desorbed from the adsorbent bands with chloroform. The separated extracts were weighed and infrared spectra prepared to provide the following identifications (Table 42).

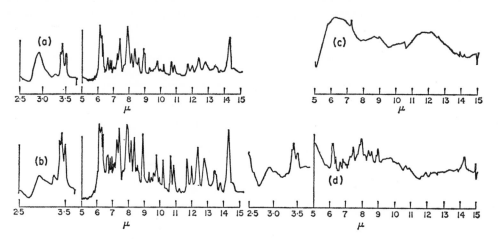

FIG. 52. Infrared spectrum of UV 531 (2-hydroxy-4-octoxy benzophenone) isolated from polyolefin nibs (potassium bromide discs).

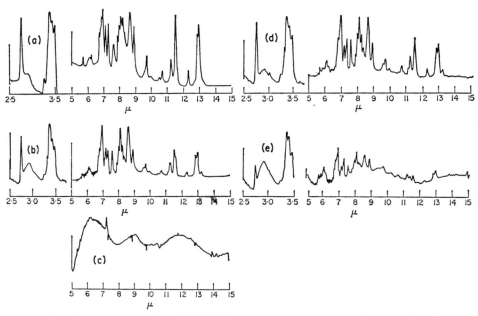

FIG. 53. Infrared spectra of Ionol CP and its degradation product isolated from polyolefin (potassium bromide discs).

TABLE 42.

R_f	% in polymer	Type of additive	
0·0	1·5	RCON⟨ $(CH_2)_2$ OOCR / $(CH_2)_2$ OH	
0·45	0·5	⬡ ⟨ COO Ph / COO Ph	
0·8	2·0	RCOOR'	Alcohol ester of saturated fatty acid, (R alkyl)
0·9	2·5	C_nH_{2n+2}	Higher molecular weight paraffin

CHAPTER 4

APPLICATION OF GAS CHROMATOGRAPHY

4.1 Characterization and Determination of Additives

The attraction of gas chromatography lies in its ability to simultaneously separate, identify and estimate sub-milligram quantities of complex mixtures. There are certain drawbacks to the technique. Retention times are no more specific for gas chromatography than are R_f values for thin-layer and paper chromatography. Day-to-day reproducibility of retention times is not good for some types of instruments, especially when operating at high column temperatures. Since many polymer additives are not very volatile, low stationary-phase loadings have to be used in order to reduce retention times to a sensible value, which means that large areas of uncoated solid support appear which in turn lead to bonding with compounds such as phenolic and amine antioxidants. This results in distortion of peaks and in lengthening of retention times. There are measures which can be taken to meet these difficulties. Thus, relative retention times are often more reproducible than unadjusted retention times. Non-volatile sample components can be converted into more volatile derivatives such as tri-methyl-silyl ethers.[219] The solid support can also be treated with hexamethyldisilazane,[220] for example, to reduce the number of active sites on the column material available for bonding. The formation of derivatives before chromatography does, however, in some applications lead to sample loss and can often lead to the appearance of spurious peaks on the chromatogram. Nevertheless, despite these limitations gas chromatography has found numerous applications in the identification, characterization and estimation of additives in polymers and some of these are discussed below in further detail.

Gas chromatography is particularly useful for the characterization of more volatile substances such as mixtures of fatty acids or of alcohols, esters or hydrocarbons which are used in polymer formulations. It has the advantage that it provides more information regarding the carbon number distribution of each of these types of compounds than can be obtained by infrared spectroscopy alone. Similarly, if the polymer is known or suspected to contain dicarboxylic acids,[206] polyol esters,[207] polyhydric alcohols[208] or alcohol esters of phthalic, sebacic, adipic or azelaic acids, then, frequently, information on the type of compound present can be obtained by comparing under the same conditions the retention time of the unknown with those of known authentic substances.

Wheeler[22] has reviewed gas chromatographic methods for the separation of amine and phenolic type antioxidants (Table 43).

Roberts and Swank[293] describe a procedure for the determination of Ionol (2,6-di-tert-butyl-*p*-cresol) and Tinuvin P (hydroxyphenylbenzotriazole) in polystyrene. In this

TABLE 43. SEPARATION OF ANTIOXIDANTS—GAS LIQUID CHROMATOGRAPHIC TECHNIQUES

Substances separated	Stationary phase	Column temp. °C	Other details	Refs.
2,6-Di-t-butyl-*p*-cresol, 2-(2-Hydroxy-5-methyl-phenyl) benzotriazole	25% LAC-2R/446 (adipate ester) +2% H_3PO_4 on chromosorb	135	H_2 carrier gas, F.I.D. Error ±1%	194
2,6-Di-t-butyl-*p*-cresol, (I) 2,6-Di-t-butyl phenol 2,4,6-tri-t-butyl phenol Diphenylamine	10% Apiezon N on celite 545	164	H_2 carrier, F.I.D. 10^{-3} M (I) in presence of others can be detected	221
2,6-Di-t-butyl-*p*-cresol Phenyl-2-naph-thylamine	Apiezon		F.I.D.	222
Halogenated bis-phenols	10% DC-710 Silicone oil on chromoport 80–100 mesh	225–250	12 in. glass column ¼ in. o.d. Carrier: 130 ml He/min	200
Low b.p. phenols	Capillary column coated with 10% xylenol phosphate	125	F.I.D.	202
Phenol and 5-t-butyl derivatives	Silicone oil 550-carbowax 400 (3:2)	200	Mean deviation 0·4%	197
Phenols and cresols	5% w/w of various phosphate esters of phenols	110	120 cm × 4·5 mm column, Pye-Argon Chromatograph	198
Ionox 330 see text	(a) 20% DC-710 Silicone oil on chromosorb. (b) 2% SE.30 Silicone gum on chromosorb mesh	200–300 in. 10 min.	(a) 12 × 3/16 in. column (b) 12 × 1/16 in. stainless steel column	216
Low molecular weight phenols	Silicone-coated capillary column		Converted to trimethyl-silyl esters before chromatography.	219
2,6-Di-4-methyl phenol	20% SE.30 on HMDS-treated 60 mesh chromosorb W	200	E.C. detector	220

HMDS, hexamethyldisilazane. E.C., electron capture. F.I.D., flame ionization detector.

procedure the polymer is dissolved in a low boiling solvent such as methylene dichloride and injected directly into the chromatograph. Buttery and Stuckey[304] describe the determination of butylated hydroxy anisole and butylated hydroxy toluene on a Apiezon L column at 220°C. Jennings *et al.*[305, 306] describe a method for the determination of Ionol (2,6-di-tert-butyl-*p*-cresol) in paperboard involving a preliminary extraction with a cyclohexane/iso-propanol mixture followed by chromatography on a propylene glycol column at 200°C.

Schröder and Rudolph[217] utilized gas chromatography for the quantitative determination of phenolic antioxidants in polyethylene. They used either Dow-Corning silicone oil 550 or Apiezon L as a mobile phase. A chloroform solution of the polyethylene extract was injected into the column at column temperatures of 220°C for the silicone oil and 190°C for Apiezon L. Hydrogen was used as carrier gas. Compounds such as 2-tert-butyl-4-methyl phenol, 2,6-di-tert-butyl-4-methyl phenol and p-tert-butyl phenol were estimated in polyethylene with good precision and in amounts down to 0·5% in the original polymer, using this procedure.

Knight and Siegel[216] have shown that programmed temperature gas chromatography between 200° and 300°C on a silicone elastomer coated column can elute phenolic antioxidants of very high molecular weight and boiling point. Thus, they successfully eluted Ionox 330 (1,3,5-tri-methyl-2,4,6-tri-(3,5-di-t-butyl-4-hydroxyl benzyl) benzene), which has a molecular weight of 775. They applied this method to the determination of Ionox 330 in various polymers. The conditions used by Knight[216] are given below:

Chromatograph	Aerograph Model 600-C with flame ionization detector.
Column	$\frac{1}{8}$ in. × 18 in. stainless steel with 5% SE-30, Silicone Gum Rubber, Methyl, General Electric Co., on 80/90 Anakrom ABS (acrylonitrile–butadienestyrene), Analabs, Inc.
Temperatures	
Injection port	330°C
Column	290°C
Detector	290°C
Carrier gas	65 ml/min helium
Retention time for Ionox 330	8·5 min

Calibration standards representing 0·1 g/l. to 0·8 g/l. Ionox 330 were analysed with an average repeatability of ±2·0%. The calibration curve obtained as a plot of peak area versus concentration was linear and passed through the origin, indicating that no Ionox 330 is lost through decomposition in the hot injection port.

Zulaicka and Guichon[294, 295] analysed the adipates and phthalates of n-alcohols on columns packed with glass beads coated with either silicone oil or neopentyl glycol polysebacate. They resolved esters boiling up to 400°C. By analysing several homologous series of esters on both polar and non-polar liquid phases these workers were able to establish that a relationship existed between the refractive index of the ester and the retention index of the corresponding alcohol and acid parts of the ester molecule. Zulaicka et al.[296] made a detailed study on a polymethyl-siloxane column of the adipates and phthalates of the n-alkanes and applied the method to commercial products. Guichon and Henniker[297] also refer to the qualitative analysis of plasticizers. Zulaicka and Guichon[298] describe a technique whereby adipate and phthalate plasticizers are mildly pyrolysed at the gas chromatograph injection port thereby eliminating the need for a solvent extraction procedure on the polymer sample. Cook et al.[302] describe the gas chromatography of benzyl butyl phthalate and related plasticizers on a silicone grease column of 235°C. Haslam et al.[289] employed a procedure based on pyrolysis for the determination of polyethyl esters in methacrylate copolymers. The alkoxy groups in the polymers were pyrolysed to their corresponding alkyl iodides which were then determined by chromatography on a dinonyl sebacate column at 75°C. Similarly, Miller[303] determined acrylate ester impurities in polymers by converting the alkoxy groups to alkyl iodides which were gas chromatographed on a di-2-ethyl hexyl sebacate column at 70°C. Perry[309] has reviewed the application of pyrolysis/gas chromatography to the identification of volatile and non-volatile components of polymers. Esposito[299] identified polyhydric alcohols in resins by programmed temperature gas chromatography. Mono- and di-carboxylic acids are identified in alkyd and polyester resins by Esposito and Swann[300] who transesterify the resins to form methyl esters and then examine these on silicone grease or Carbowax columns using programmed temperature gas chromatography. Similarly, Percival[301] first removes solvent and monomer from the resin and then subjects it to methanolysis prior to gas chromatography on a Silicone SF 96 column. Esposito and Swann[285] identified esters produced from polyols present in synthetic resins, by programmed temperature gas chromatography on a Carbowax 20-M column over a temperature range 50° to 225°C. They prepared the esters by reacting the polyol with butyl amine then acetic anhydride and then extracting the reaction product with chloroform.

Wize and Sullivan[215, 310] have used high temperature gas chromatography for the analysis of mixtures of amine type antidegradants in rubber. They used a separation column constructed of aluminium packed with 20% Apiezon L on 30–60 mesh chromasorb W. Analysis was carried out on an acetone extract of the rubber sample, employing diphenyl amine as an internal standard. Using column temperatures up to 310°C they were able to separate a range of antidegradants including 1,2-dihydroxy-2,2,4-tri-methyl-6-ethoxy-quinaline, N-isopropyl-N'-phenyl-p-phenylenediamine, N-phenyl-2-naphthylamine, N,N'-di-2-octyl-p-phenylene diamine and N,N'-diphenyl-p-phenylenediamine. Near quantitative determinations were obtained for all these substances. Apiezon L was found to be distinctly superior as a mobile phase to other substances tried. Thus Dow-Corning 710 Silicone fluid and butanediol succinate were too volatile at operating temperatures up to 310°C, whilst silicone rubber, although sufficiently non-volatile, did not give the high degree of resolution obtained with Apiezon L.

Sometimes a component of a polymer extract is insufficiently volatile to elute on a gas chromatographic column, yet the hydrolysis products of this compound are volatile enough to be gas chromatographed. Thus, a surface coating on polystyrene beads, which had been isolated by shaking the polymer with methanol, was shown by preliminary infrared measurements to consist of a mixture of a metal salt of a fatty acid and a primary aliphatic amide. The metal salt was non-volatile and could not be chromatographed and the amide decomposed to a nitrile on the column. The methanol surface extract of the polymer was evaporated to dryness, weighed, and its nitrogen content determined. The residue was hydrolysed by refluxing for 6 hr with 30% sulphuric acid and free fatty acids then extracted with benzene. Gas chromatography of this extract showed that it consisted almost entirely of three groups of carboxylic acids, each with its own carbon number distribution as follows:

(i) $C_2 - C_{15}$ Mainly palmitic acid 40%
(ii) $C_{16} - C_{17}$ Mainly stearic acid 30%
(iii) C_{21} Erucic acid 25%

The original polymer surface coating therefore probably consisted of a mixture of a metal stearate, erucic acid and palmitamide. This assumption leads to a nitrogen content of 2·3% whereas the nitrogen content found was 2·1%. This type of hydrolysis technique can be applied to other types of compounds which might be difficult to chromatograph in their original form. Thus, either acid or alkaline hydrolysis will convert alkanolamine/fatty acid condensates to the fatty acid and the free alkanolamine. Plasticizer esters are converted to the acid and alcohol which are often easier to identify than the original ester. Other types of compounds, which might be amenable to this approach, include aliphatic amides, sugar esters, and other types of esters such as esters of phosphorous acid, e.g. Polygard (tris-2:3-dibromopropyl phosphite).

Identification of Additives by Combination of Gas Chromatography and Infrared Spectroscopy

Some of the limitations encountered in applying gas chromatography to the unequivocal identification of polymer additives have already been discussed at the beginning of this chapter. In addition to these limitations there are others. Retention times are purely relative and not always exactly reproducible; even when the chemical class of the sample constituents is known, identification by comparison of the retention time of the unknown with those of standards requires exact reproduction of column operating conditions.

Difficulty can also arise when non-symmetrical peaks are produced; the peak-maximum retention time of a component then depends on concentration. Peaks can also overlap, and certain combinations of substances are often difficult to separate. Chromatographically, a single peak is no criterion of purity, since more than one substance may be present; the components present could often be resolved if their presence was suspected and alternative column operating conditions were selected.

Confirmation of homogeneity of fractions is therefore required together with unequivocal identification and accurate quantitative determination of the product. The analytical method used should involve some property of the molecule other than boiling-point. Often, only fractional milligram amounts of material can be recovered from a column. Of the few techniques that are applicable to these small quantities of material, mass and infrared spectroscopy are particularly suited.

The use of fraction collecting techniques in conjunction with gas chromatography is now well established[223-227, 248, 251] and is an attractive proposition in additive identification problems, despite the fact that little published work has yet appeared on the application of this technique to polymer additives.

In this technique, the separated compound as it emerges from the gas chromatographic column is swept by the carrier gas through a cold trap where it condenses. The material in the trap is then either transferred to an infrared gas cell for examination in the vapour phase, is transferred as a liquid to a suitable micro cell or may be condensed on a cold surface as a solid for examination by conventional spectroscopic techniques.

In the past few years improvements in commercially available equipment have been made which permit infrared spectroscopic examination of gas chromatographic fractions of less than 1 mg in quantity. Beam condensers to focus the energy beam of infrared spectrometers in an area of 1 mm × 5 mm[259] or smaller[255] enable the use of smaller infrared cells and potassium bromide pressed plates[249, 255] than before. Infrared cells have been developed which require only a milligram or less of liquid to fill them.[239, 245, 252, 259] Techniques and apparatus for trapping and transfer of milligram and smaller quantities of separated fractions to infrared cells have been developed.[242, 245, 252, 259] Of these the ultra-micro cavity cell manufactured by Connecticut Instrument Corporation is particularly noteworthy. These are made by ultrasonically drilling cavities in rectangular blocks of sodium chloride. The Type "D" "ultra-micro" cavity cell has a sample area of 1 mm × 4·5 mm and cell thicknesses between 0·05 mm and 1 mm. Beckman Instruments

Inc. sell "ultra-micro" cavity cells in several thicknesses between 0·1 mm and 0·025 mm. In general these cells have disadvantages compared to those made available by Connecticut Instrument Company. Research and Industrial Instruments Company, London, supply a micro cell in which the collection of the gas chromatographic fraction and the spectrum run are carried out in the same cell without the sample actually being handled. These cells have path lengths between 0·01 and 0·10 mm and a minimum capacity of 0·2 μl. The cells are extruded in one piece from silver chloride and are unaffected by water or most organic or inorganic solvents. The system may be applied to the collection of low and high boiling liquids as well as solid GC fractions which may be examined in the neat or solvent diluted condition.

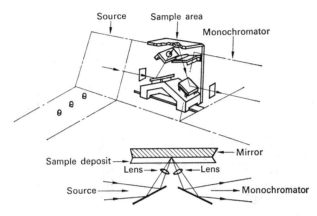

FIG. 54. Infrared spectroscopy of microsized samples. (*Top*) optical path through micro specular reflectance (MSR) accessory; (*Bottom*) optical path through transparent sample mounted in MSR accessory.[232]

Cells have also been described for infrared spectroscopy of fractions while still vaporized in the gas stream emerging from the gas chromatographic column[253, 258] and also for obtaining the vapour spectra of fractions after trapping and revaporizing them.[233, 237, 245]

Trapping of gas chromatographic fractions in dry-ice cooled glass[250] or metal[252] capillary tubes is fairly efficient for high boiling compounds, decreasing in efficiency with lower boiling substances. Presumably, with the lower boiling substances, losses are due to some of the gas chromatographic fraction being swept through the trap as a fog or as frozen particles.[257] When helium is used as the carrier gas it is possible that small amounts of helium impurities, notably water,[242] can be trapped out together with the gas chromatographic fraction. In these circumstances it is necessary to carefully dry the carrier gas entering the gas chromatograph in order to eliminate any interference effects in the subsequent infrared spectroscopy of trapped fractions.

Various other workers have described techniques for collecting individual gas chromatographic fractions and transferring these as liquids to micro infrared cells. These include Grasselli and Snavely[230] who claim to be able to examine 0·4 μl of a liquid sample in the infrared without the use of beam condensers. They claim their fraction trapping technique is efficient enough to permit quantitative collection of fractions. Blake *et al.*[231] describe a similar technique for collecting and obtaining the infrared spectra of gas chromatographic fractions in the 10–100 μg range. The equipment is simple, inexpensive, and spectra may be scanned with a simple table top infrared spectrometer without beam condensers using a cell made by drilling a 1 mm diameter hole in a cube of sodium chloride.

Sloane *et al.*[232] describe a specular reflectance system for the infrared analysis of micro-sized samples. They compare the advantages and limitations of this technique with other micro infrared techniques. Samples are mounted on small metal mirrors (Fig. 54) which reflect the light beam back through the sample. A transmission spectrum is thereby obtained but the effective path length is twice that of the actual sample thickness and a given absorption band consequently has twice the absorbance obtained by conventional transmission

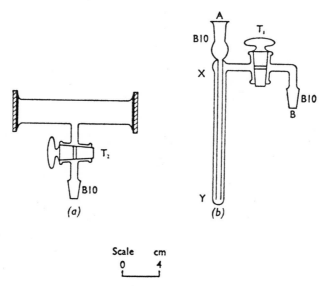

Scale   cm
0   4

FIG. 55. Trap for collecting products separated by gas chromatography, Anderson.[218]

measurements. This system was applied successfully to gas chromatographic fractions, and is claimed to be particularly useful for the examination of non-volatile liquids such as, for example, dioctyl phthalate. Crystalline solids are easily deposited and handled on the metal mirrors, but crystallinity effects on the spectrum must be carefully watched out for. Its limitations include a "stray-light" artefact, polymorphism effects and difficulties in obtaining sample uniformity.

Anderson[218] has described in detail a technique for collecting individual products separated from mixtures by gas chromatography and the subsequently used technique for their identification by vapour phase infrared spectroscopy using a Hilger H800 double beam spectrometer. The trap and infrared cell used by Anderson are shown in Fig. 55. He claimed that the technique would identify and determine; to within $\pm 2\%$, amounts as low as 5 μmoles of all substances having a boiling point up to about 175°C. Heated gas cells enable liquids of higher boiling point to be examined. Naturally, as the infrared spectrum of a compound in the liquid and vapour form are different, it is necessary to compare spectra obtained by the above technique with spectra of standard vapours. Generally speaking, the additive constituents of polymers have a boiling point which is appreciably higher than 200°C and hence cannot be handled in infrared gas cells. For such substances, infrared examination as a liquid or a solid, as is discussed below, is more relevant. Obviously, in order to avoid volatilization during polymer processing and subsequent life, most types of additives used in polymer formulations are fairly high melting point solids. Volatile constituents are, however, sometimes encountered, viz. expanding agents, plasticizers, lubricants, adhesives, solvents, monomers and degradation products of additives or of the polymer itself, and infrared gas cell techniques can be of value in the examination of gas chromatographic fractions containing these types of substances.

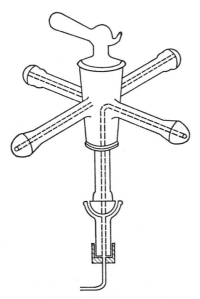

FIG. 56. Tap to which four collection traps may be attached[228] used for trapping of gas chromatographic fractions.

Haslam *et al.*[228] have studied in detail the collection of volatile and liquid fractions emerging from a gas chromatographic column and their subsequent identification by infrared spectroscopy. They applied these techniques to various polymeric materials encountered in the plastics industry. They incorporated several of the techniques developed by Anderson[227] into their procedures, but, unlike him, found that his technique could not be applied effectively to substances with a boiling point much in excess of 120°C. Moreover, they found that many of the standard infrared spectra of substances encountered in the plastics industry were recorded only for liquid compounds and not for the corresponding vapours.

All the fraction-collecting apparatus described by Haslam[228] is used in conjunction with gas-chromatographic columns operated under reduced pressure and with katharometer detection. This gas-chromatographic equipment is of two types.

Type 1. Apparatus involving a column thermostatically controlled within the range 0° to 130°C and a katharometer at room temperature. This apparatus is used for separating mixtures when the highest-boiling constituent boils below 160°C at atmospheric pressure.

Type 2. Apparatus involving a column and katharometer contained within the same thermostatically controlled chamber and maintained at some temperature in the range 100° to 200°C. This apparatus is used for the separation of mixtures with constituents boiling up to 250°C, which give trouble in apparatus of type 1 owing to condensation in the katharometer.

The trap shown in Figs. 57 and 58 (see later) has been successfully used with apparatus of type 1 for the condensation of substances boiling in the range −100° to +160°C. The packing used is small Dixon rings held in place by a small loose-fitting piece of glass rod. The efficiency of this type of trap varies between 85 and 95%, depending on the chemical class of substance. Figure 56 shows a four-way tap to which four such traps may be attached. The tap is connected to the exit of the katharometer by means of the minimum length of stainless-steel tubing (internal diameter 1 mm) brazed into a metal cup. This in turn is cemented to a glass socket with Araldite cement. The exit ends of the four traps are connected via rubber tubing and separate stopcocks to a vacuum manifold. The traps are partly immersed in liquid nitrogen contained in 1-pint Thermos flasks.

A preliminary chromatogram indicates the complexity of the mixture. On a second run, the traps are switched in by following the recorder trace and any overlap between peaks is allowed to go to waste. The delay time between the recorder signal and the component reaching the trap is negligible.

Having condensed the desired component in a trap it has to be decided whether to record the spectrum in the vapour state (method 1 below) or the liquid phase (method 2 below). Anderson's method[227] is retained for identifying all components that, from the gas-chromatographic evidence, would appear to boil below 60°C. Small amounts of such substances in liquid form are readily lost by vaporization in attempting the transfer to a small liquid infrared cell.

Haslam et al.[228] developed four techniques for infrared examination of gas chromatographic effluents.

Method 1. Liquids of boiling point up to 60°C

Figure 57 shows how the low-boiling component is transferred to the infrared gas cell. The design of the apparatus is different, but the procedure for transference is identical to that described by Anderson[227] except that no heat is applied to the trap.

The infrared gas cell is designed to obtain the strongest possible absorption from a small amount of sample. The intensity of absorption depends only on the number of molecules in the path of the radiation beam; this is increased by reducing the cross-sectional area of the cell, which, however, must not be reduced to an extent such that the energy transmitted is insufficient to record the spectrum. The intensity may also be increased by passing the beam several times through the same volume of gas, as in reflecting cells of the type described by White et al.[229] Unfortunately, these cells are difficult to construct and must be specially designed for a particular instrument. Consequently Haslam[228] used an efficient straight single-pass cell.

In order to attain optimum light transmission, such a cell is inserted at a point where the area of the spectrometer beam is least; this will be where a focus of the beam is formed in the centre of the cell. At a few centimetres on either side of the focal position the beam is rectangular; this, therefore, is the most economical shape for the cell. To decide the dimensions of the cell it was assumed that 1 ml of gas at N.T.P. would be available. Condensation of liquids boiling up to 100°C may occur on the walls of the cell at pressures above 80 mm; the cell must therefore be of capacity about 9 ml.

The image to be found in the centre of the cell should normally have the length and width of the entrance slit of the spectrometer. Knowing the f number of the instrument it is possible to calculate the size of the rectangular aperture required to admit the radiation cone in terms of the length of the cell. For the instrument used (Hilger H800, aperture f 11) the dimensions for a 9-ml cell are: length, 10 cm; height, 1·5 cm; width, 0·6 cm (Fig. 57). The body consists of rectangular brass tube (1 mm thick) cut from wave-guide tubing and has the internal dimensions stated above. A flat brass flange is brazed on each end of the tube, and a short side-arm (stainless-steel capillary tubing) is brazed in one side of the body. A glass capillary tap that will just slide over the side-arm is cemented in place by filling the space between the two tubes with Araldite resin; by this means, the volume of the side-arm is

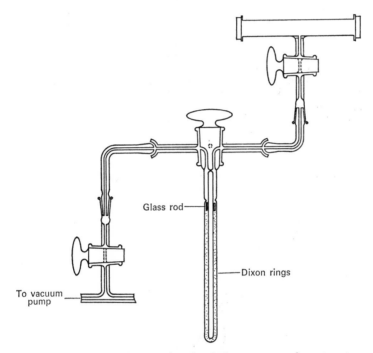

Glass rod

Dixon rings

To vacuum pump

FIG. 57. Apparatus for transfer of volatile component from trap to infrared gas cell.[228]

rendered negligible. Two rock-salt windows are attached to the flanges with Picene wax. Although the cell is designed for an f 11 system, it will give acceptable performance, although with some loss of energy, on an f 7 spectrometer.

Method 2. Liquids boiling above 60°C

If the gas-chromatographic evidence indicates that the substance boils above 60°C, the fraction condensed in the trap is treated as shown in Fig. 58. The trap and contents are held in liquid nitrogen while the apparatus is completely evacuated. After testing the system for leaks, the source of vacuum is cut off. The flask containing the liquid nitrogen is removed from the trap and placed over the side-arm so that the bulb is just immersed in the refrigerant. As the trap attains room temperature, the small amount of liquid in it distils through the desiccant and is condensed round the sides of the bulb of the side-arm. The liquid is encouraged into the capillary tip by lowering the vacuum flask containing the liquid nitro-gen until only the last ¼ in. of the tip is immersed. The bulb is then warmed with the fingers. During this distillation the trap is not warmed, as this may cause some of the liquid to distil in the wrong direction. The apparatus may be left for 1 or 2 hr in order to achieve complete

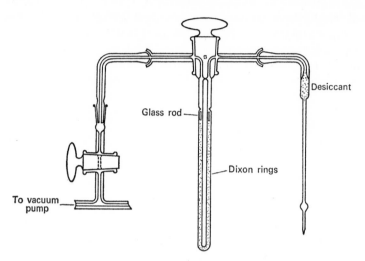

FIG. 58. Apparatus for transfer of liquid component from trap to tip
of side-arm[228]

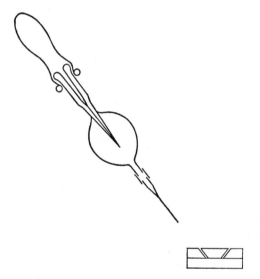

FIG. 59. Pipette for transferring liquid to
micro infrared cell.[228]

distillation of higher-boiling liquids. Having obtained the liquid in the capillary tip, this tip is broken off at the constriction just below the bulb. Figure 59 shows a piece of apparatus which may be used to transfer the liquid to the micro infrared cell. It has a rubber teat and a very fine internal capillary. The device has a detachable tip, which is discarded after use and permits close control over the transfer operation. In the design of a small liquid cell, first consideration must be given to reducing the cross-sectional area, the precise area required for a particular spectrometer being found by trial and error. The radiation beam of the instrument is obstructed at the cell-mounting position, to find the least dimensions at which workable energy transmission is retained. A cross-section of 5 mm × 1·5 mm is suitable for the Hilger H800 spectrometer, although the resulting cell could be used satisfactorily on other instruments, namely, the Perkin-Elmer 21, the Perkin-Elmer 137 (Infracord) and the Grubb-Parsons GS2A.

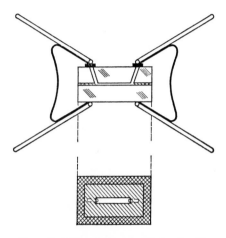

Fig. 60. Micro infrared cell for liquid
samples.[228]

Most of the sample placed in a normal infrared liquid cell is used in the filling tubes rather than in the area exposed to the beam. Consideration was therefore given to a cell in which the filling tubes need not be occupied with liquid, and a suitable design is shown in Fig. 60. The two rock-salt plates are about 20 mm × 10 mm × 3 mm in size. Two holes are drilled in one plate with a No. 86 drill; these holes taper inwards, as shown, being 7 mm apart on the inside and 12 mm apart on the outside of the plate. A gold-foil washer (25 μ thick) is cut, the inner space being 1·5 mm wide and approximately 7 mm in length (just sufficient to clear the edges of the filling holes); the width of this washer is about 2 mm. The cell is first stuck together with gold amalgam. The washer is immersed in mercury for a short period and withdrawn after a layer of amalgam has formed on its surface. The cell is then carefully assembled in a small clamp and left under pressure for 24 hr for the amalgam to set. The space between the plates outside the washer is then filled with Araldite 700 resin and a reasonable surplus of resin is allowed to bridge the edges of the plates on all four sides. The resin was found to be necessary, as the gold amalgam is a poor adhesive and the cell tends to open up and channel; the amalgam joint acts as a barrier to prevent the resin from contaminating the cell window.

The cell is filled by inserting a capillary needle containing the liquid into one filling hole. Provided that the thickness of the cell is less than the diameter of the needle, the liquid will run in to fill the cell area. It is essential that no free space be left in the cell behind the filling holes; such space will not immediately fill by capillary action and air bubbles trapped here may subsequently run into the useful part of the cell and are most difficult to remove. When the cell is filled, the outer ends of the filling tubes are covered by two small squares of nitrile-rubber sheet, held in position by "butterfly" spring clips. This method forms an excellent seal without displacing the contents of the cell by air pressure, as may occur with stoppers that are pushed or screwed into the filling tubes.

The amount of liquid required to fill the cell by the method described above (as opposed to the theoretical capacity of the cell calculated from the dimensions) is determined experimentally by weighing the cell on a microbalance before and after filling. For six fillings with α-dodecane (density 0·766) the weights recorded were 0·53, 0·36, 0·27, 0·29, 0·67 and 0·31 mg. This compares with the calculated capacity of 0·20 mg of n-dodecane ($7 \times 1·5 \times 0·025 \times 0·766$). With this cell, infrared spectra have been obtained from 0·5 to 1·0 μl portions of liquid samples, but practice is required in the transfer of these small volumes. On the other hand, 2 to 3 μl of liquid present no difficulties.

Method 3

This is an extremely simple, but effective, method that has been used in conjunction with a Griffin and George mark II gas chromatograph. The back plate of the oven is removed and the copper pipe ($\frac{1}{8}$ in. internal diameter) from the katharometer is cut, leaving approximately $\frac{1}{2}$ in. protruding beyond the oven wall. An Agla syringe barrel containing a tiny piece of cotton-wool (2 to 3 mg) is connected into the exit-gas stream by sleeving one end of the barrel over the copper pipe with silicone-rubber tubing. This entails running a preliminary chromatogram and "breaking into" the gas stream at the appropriate point in the chromatogram on a second run. The piece of cotton-wool, although not particularly efficient, has the effect of stopping "vapour fog" from passing straight through the barrel. The syringe barrel is cooled during this operation by packing solid carbon dioxide round the outside. Having wetted the cotton-wool with the unidentified component, the syringe barrel is removed from the gas stream and a specially adapted nozzle is inserted. This nozzle consists of a fine piece of hypodermic tubing sleeved and cemented into the normal Agla glass nozzle and filed flush with the glass at one end. This has the effect of cutting down the "dead" volume of the syringe to the minimum. The syringe is held nozzle uppermost, the piston is inserted and the air expelled. The sample is then expressed from the cotton-wool by pressure of the piston directly into the micro infrared liquid cell.

Unfortunately, it has been found that 10 to 12 μl of sample are needed in order to express sufficient liquid to fill the cell. However, if insufficient liquid is available, a drop of carbon disulphide is placed on the cotton-wool from a second syringe and the carbon disulphide solution of the sample is expressed into the cell.

This method proved valuable in the examination of a sample of acrylic sheet known from elemental analysis to contain phosphorus. Dry vacuum distillation of the polymer and solvent extraction both yielded a liquid, which, on direct infrared examination, proved to be an impure material containing phosphate or phosphite. The vacuum distillate at 200°C was submitted to gas-liquid chromatographic examination on a 6-ft ($\frac{1}{4}$ in. diameter) column packed with 30% w/w of silicone E301 on Celite maintained at 130°C. A sample of the main component was taken by method 3 and the infrared spectrum obtained was readily identified as that of triethyl phosphate.

In a modification of method 3, Haslam et al.[228] fitted a heated outlet pipe to the back of the katharometer and condensed the vapour in the trap shown in Fig. 61. The outlet pipe consists of a stainless-steel tube (1 mm internal diameter) approximately 9 in. long and terminates in a brass plug tapered to fit a B7 cone. The opposite end is joined to the copper exit pipe of the katharometer with silicone-rubber tubing The pipe is heated directly by passing approximately 0·5 V at 10 A through it from a variable transformer. The lagging is of asbestos string and fire clay cement covered by a second layer of asbestos string.

The trap is connected into the gas stream at the appropriate point in the chromatogram. The lower part of the trap is immersed in liquid nitrogen and the fraction condensed. The subsequent procedure is similar to that described for method 2, the small amount of substance being vacuum-distilled into the tip, which is then broken off, and the liquid is transferred to the micro infrared cell.

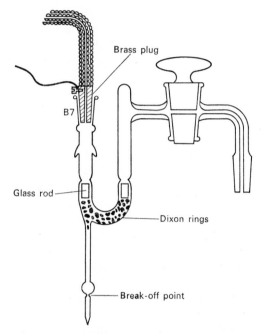

FIG. 61. Trap used for collection of fractions emerging from gas chromatographic column.[228]

Mass spectrometric examination of fractions separated by gas chromatography has been used by a number of investigators,[240, 254] for identification and quantitative analysis. This technique could undoubtedly be used in the solution of additive identification problems.

4.2 Characterization and Determination of Monomers and Volatile Impurities

Polymers often contain substances of medium volatility such as residual monomers, residual polymerization solvents and expanding agents. In addition, when polymers are heated they may release volatiles as a result of the thermal degradation of either the polymers themselves or their additives or catalyst residues. These volatiles can have an important bearing on such properties as processability, the tendency to form voids and, in the case of foodstuff-packaging grades, the possible tendency to impart taste or odour to the packed commodity.

One way of identifying non-polymeric constituents of polymers is to extract the polymer with a low-boiling-point solvent, remove the solvent from the extract by evaporation or distillation and analyse the residue. This procedure is, of course, inapplicable to the analysis of extracted polymer constituents which are volatile enough to be lost during the solvent-removal stage. Alternatively, an extract or a solution of the polymer may be examined directly for volatile constituents by gas chromatography, in which case losses of volatiles are less likely to occur.

In such a procedure, however, the large excess of solvent used for extraction or solution might interfere with the interpretation of the chromatogram, obscuring some of the peaks of interest. Trace impurities in the solvent may also interfere with the chromatogram. Of course, none of these procedures is suitable for studying the nature of volatile breakdown products which are produced only upon heating a polymer.

A simple and inexpensive apparatus has been described by Crompton and Myers[260] for liberating both existing volatiles and those produced by thermal degradation from polymers by heating at temperatures up to 300°C, in the absence of solvents, prior to their examination by gas chromatography. The technique avoids the disadvantages resulting from the use of extraction or solution procedures.

The apparatus illustrated in Fig. 62 consists of a glass ignition tube, supported as shown in a Wade $\frac{1}{4}$-in. diameter brass coupling nut, covered with a silicone rubber spectrum and sealed with a Wade $\frac{1}{4}$-in. brass stop-end body. The stop-end body has two 1-mm diameter holes drilled through the cap. The whole unit is placed in a slot in a cylindrical copper block (3 in. long × 2 in. dia.) which is heated by two (240 V, 85 W) cartridge heaters and controlled at temperatures up to 300°C from a variable transformer. The temperature is measured with a thermocouple capable of accurately measuring temperatures in the 100–300°C temperature range with a maximum error of $\pm 5\%$. The thermocouple is inserted in the slot adjacent to the ignition tube; it has been shown that under these conditions the thermocouple records the true temperature of the contents of the tube. The provision of a slot in the copper block enables more than one ignition tube to be heated simultaneously if required.

A sample of the polymer (0·25–0·50 g) is placed in an ignition tube and sealed with Wade fittings and a septum, as described. If necessary, the tube is then purged with a suitable gas by inserting two hypodermic needles through the septum via the holes in the cap of the stop-end body and passing the gas into the tube through one hole and allowing it to vent through the other. After purging, the two needles are removed simultaneously and the tube is then heated in the copper block under the required conditions of time and temperature. A sample (1–2 ml) of the head-space gas is withdrawn from the ignition tube into a Hamilton gas-tight hypodermic syringe via the septum and injected into a gas chromatograph. It is advisable to fill the syringe with the gas used initially in the ignition tube and to inject this into the tube before withdrawing the sample. This facilitates sampling by preventing the creation of a partial vacuum in the ignition tube or the syringe, or both. It also minimizes any undesirable entry of air into the ignition tube.

With the apparatus, a polymer may be heated under any desired gas and, while this may frequently be the carrier gas used with the gas chromatograph, it is also possible to carry out studies in oxidizing or reducing atmospheres. A polymer may also be heated to any temperature and samples of the head-space gas may be withdrawn at intermediate temperatures and times to determine under what conditions any particular volatile is liberated.

By using gas chromatographic detectors of suitable sensitivities and selectivities, it is possible to examine polymers for the presence or formation of volatiles at both the percentage and the parts-per-million levels. For example, traces of organic volatiles may be examined with an ionization detector, and traces of organic halogen compounds lend themselves to analysis with an electron capture detector. Thermal conductivity cells of the hot-wire or thermistor type are suitable for the detection of inorganic volatiles, and a helium ionization detector could be used for analysing trace amounts of permanent gases.

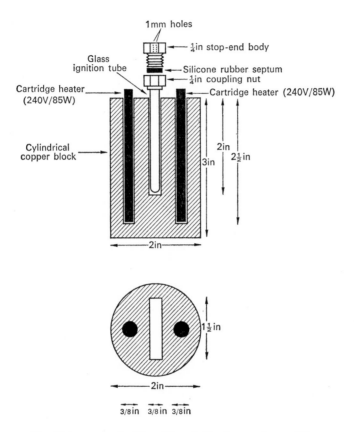

FIG. 62 Apparatus for liberating volatiles from polymers.[260]

Analysis of Volatiles from Polyethylene

Polyethylene is not appreciably soluble in organic solvents, and the determination of existing volatile impurities cannot be conveniently carried out by the analysis of solutions of the polymer. Many organic solvents will extract such volatiles from polyethylene, but these are likely to be lost during the solvent-removal stage prior to gas chromatographic analysis. A further problem is that extraction procedures cannot be used for investigating those volatiles that are not inherently present but are produced only when the polymer is heated. The following examples illustrate the use of the method for examining both types of volatiles released from polyethylene.

The technique was used to study the effect of temperature on the nature of the volatiles released, and to investigate this polyethylene was heated for 15 min in air at 125°, 150°,

175° and 200°C and the volatiles were examined by gas chromatography. Figure 63 shows the chromatograms of the volatiles released at 125° and 200°C, and Table 44 gives the peak height ratios of the major components (1–7) released at all four temperatures. Replicate runs indicated good reproducibility.

The results in Table 44 show that the only significant variation of peak height ratios with temperature occurs when component 1 is compared with components 2–7 and component 2 is compared with components 4–7. As the temperature increases to 200°C, components 1 and 2 increase while components 3–7 decrease (Fig. 63). Components 1 and 2 were eluted in the C_2–C_4 hydrocarbon region and components 3–7 were eluted coincident with the major

TABLE 44. PEAK HEIGHT RATIOS OF VOLATILES LIBERATED
BY POLYETHYLENE AT VARIOUS TEMPERATURES, DETERMINED
BY GAS CHROMATOGRAPHY

Component Number Ratio	Peak Height Ratio			
	125°C	150°C	175°C	200°C
1:2	4·4	5·4	3·1	3·1
1:3	0·3	0·3	0·3	1·7
1:4	2·1	3·2	2·4	14·6
1:5	0·7	1·0	0·8	4·7
1:6	0·5	0·8	0·6	3·5
1:7	0·9	1·2	1·0	5·9
2:3	0·06	0·06	0·08	0·06
2:4	0·5	0·6	0·8	4·6
2:5	0·2	0·2	0·3	1·5
2:6	0·1	0·1	0·2	1·1
2:7	0·2	0·2	0·3	1·9
3:4	8·1	9·6	9·1	8·3
3:5	2·9	3·1	3·1	2·7
3:6	2·1	2·3	2·3	2·0
3:7	3·4	3·7	3·8	3·4
4:5	0·4	0·3	0·3	0·3
4:6	0·3	0·2	0·3	0·2
4:7	0·4	0·4	0·4	0·4
5:6	0·7	0·7	0·7	0·8
5:7	1·2	1·2	1·2	1·3
6:7	1·7	1·6	1·6	1·7

components of the polymerization solvent known to be used in this polyethylene manufacturing process. These observations suggest that between 125° and 200°C there is some thermal degradation of the polymerization solvent to C_2–C_4 hydrocarbons.

These results led to the conclusion that the major volatile components of this polyethylene were due to residual polymerization solvent. Also that, when examining polyethylene for existing volatiles, it is necessary to use as low a temperature as possible for liberating the volatiles if thermal degradation is to be avoided. A temperature of 125°C appeared to be suitable.

The gas chromatograms in Fig. 64 show that when polyethylenes from several different manufacturers were heated at 125°C for 15 min in air and the liberated volatiles were examined by gas chromatography, the chromatograms show quite noticeable differences in the nature of the volatiles produced. Those from manufacturers 1 and 2 liberate essentially low-boiling-point volatiles, whereas those from manufacturers 3, 4 and 5 liberate volatiles with a wider range of retention times.

Food and drink containers extruded or moulded from polyethylene sometimes possess unpleasant odours which are likely to taint the packaged product and are unacceptable to the consumer. In one such case it was found that by heating a sample of an odour-producing polyethylene for 15 min at 200°C under helium the chromatogram of the liberated volatiles contained certain peaks which were absent from the corresponding chromatogram from a

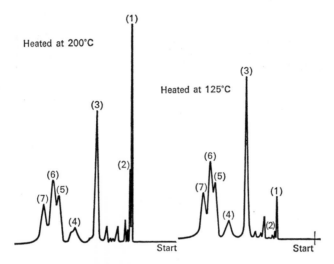

FIG. 63. Gas chromatograms of volatiles liberated from poly-ethylene heated at different temperatures for 15 min in air.[260]
Chromatographed on 200 ft × $\frac{1}{16}$ in. i.d. dibutyl-phthalate-coated copper column at 30°C and 100 ml/min helium flow, with flame ionization detection.

polyethylene which produced non-odorous food containers. The temperature of 200°C was chosen to simulate the polymer extrusion temperature. The two chromatograms are shown in Fig. 65 from which it may be seen that components A, B, D and I are present in the odorous sample but are absent from the non-odorous sample. These substances were always associated with the odorous polyethylene.

Analysis to Volatiles from Polystyrene

In Figs. 66A to E are shown gas chromatograms of volatiles obtained when polystyrenes from several different manufacturers were heated at 200°C for 15 min under helium. All the samples liberated the same range of aromatic hydrocarbons, these differing only in their relative concentrations. However, the non-aromatic hydrocarbon material, eluted from the gas chromatographic column prior to ethyl benzene, shows marked differences from sample to sample. The results do show the value of the technique for detecting differences in the volatiles liberated by polystyrenes produced by different manufacturers.

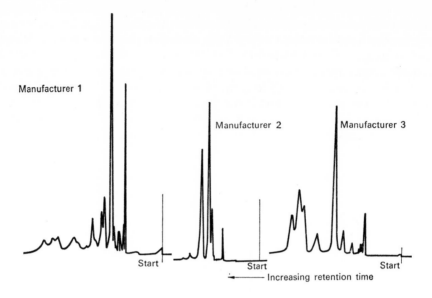

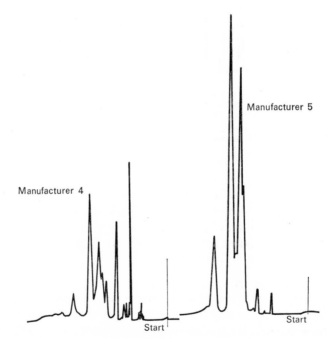

FIG. 64. Gas chromatograms of volatiles liberated from different polyethylenes at 125°C for 15 min in air.[260]

Chromatographed on 200 ft × 1/16 in. i.d. dibutyl-phthalate-coated copper column at 30°C and 100 ml/min helium flow, with flame ionization detection.

Quantitative Determination of Volatiles

Gas chromatography has been used for the quantitative determination of low levels of aromatic hydrocarbons in polystyrene, and also for the determination of expanding agents such as normal and isopentane in expandable grades of polystyrene.

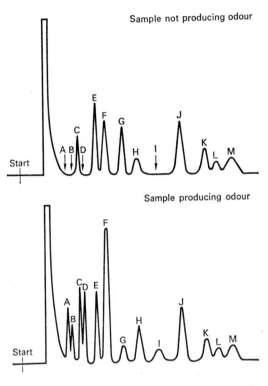

FIG. 65 Gas chromatograms of volatiles liberated from odorous and non-odorous polyethylenes at 200° C for 15 min in helium.[260]

Chromatographed on 200 ft × $\frac{1}{16}$ in. i.d. dibutyl-phthalate-coated copper column at 30°C and 100 ml/min helium flow, with flame ionization detection.

These gas chromatographic analyses are carried out on solutions of the polymers in the presence of internal standards. To avoid interferences in the analysis, it is essential for the solvent and the internal standard to have retention times different from those of the volatile compounds being determined in the polymer. Application of the volatiles apparatus described by Crompton and Myers[260] to a polystyrene provides a rapid means of determining the retention time of the volatile compounds present in the polymer, enabling a suitable solvent and internal standard to be selected for the subsequent quantitative analysis by solution procedures.

The following examples illustrate the use of the technique during the analysis of polystyrene for residual aromatic hydrocarbons and expanding agents. Figure 67 shows a chromatogram of the volatiles liberated by a polystyrene after heating at 200°C for 15 min under helium. Superimposed on the chromatogram are the solvent and internal standard

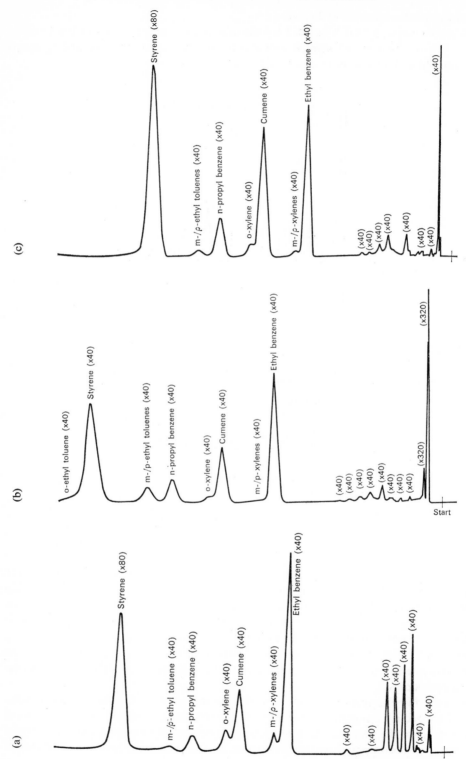

FIG. 66. Gas chromatograms of volatiles liberated from different polystyrenes at 200°C for 15 min in helium.[260]
Chromatographed on 15 ft × ⅛ in. i.d. 10% Carbowax 15–20M on 60–72 Celite at 90°C and 100 ml/min flow, with flame ionization detection. Attenuations bracketed.

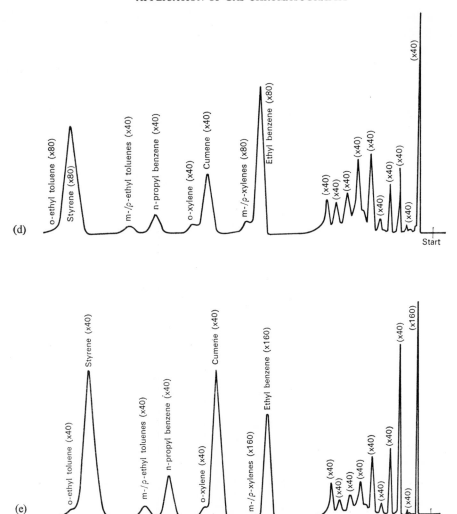

FIG. 66 (*cont.*)

peaks which would be present if the analysis were carried out on a solution of the polymer in propylene oxide in the presence of n-undecane. The quantitative determination of the aromatic hydrocarbons in polystyrene would not be interfered with by either the propylene oxide or by the n-undecane internal standard.

Mixtures of isopentane and n-pentane are commonly used as expanding agents in expandable grades of polystyrene. An available procedure for doing this involved the gas chromatographic analysis of a solution of the polymer in propylene oxide in the presence of 2:2-dimethyl butane as an internal standard. This method is entirely satisfactory for analysing grades of expandable polystyrene in which it is known that isopentane and n-pentane are the only expanding agents present. However, if other types of expanding agent have been used in the polymer formulation then it is possible that, under the selected conditions, their retention times might coincide with those of propylene oxide or 2:2-dimethyl butane, with the result that the analysis would be invalidated.

Figure 68 shows a chromatogram of the volatiles liberated by an expanded polystyrene after heating at 200°C for 15 min under helium. Superimposed on the chromatogram is the solvent peak which would be present if the analysis were carried out on a solution of the polymer in propylene oxide. In addition to n-pentane and isopentane, the sample contains lower concentrations of several C_6 and C_7 hydrocarbons, all of which originate as impurities

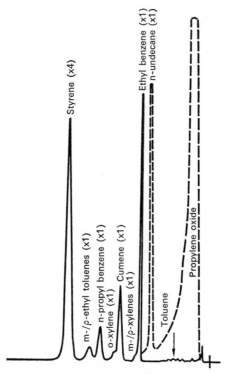

Fig. 67. Gas chromatogram of aromatic hydrocarbons liberated from polystyrene at 200°C for 15 min in helium.[260]

Chromatographed on 15 ft × $\frac{3}{16}$ in. i.d. 10% Carbo-wax 15–20M on 60–72 Celite at 90°C and 100 ml/min helium flow, with flame ionization detection.

in the pentanes used in the polystyrene formulation. One of these hydrocarbons is 2:2-dimethyl butane. Hence the presence of this substance must be allowed for by using an alternative internal standard. The chromatogram also shows that although propylene oxide would not interfere with the determination of most of the components, the n-hexane and one of the C_7 hydrocarbons would be completely obscured and could not be determined. For a complete analysis by a solution procedure it was therefore necessary to select a solvent which is eluted later than propylene oxide. Benzene was found to be suitable.

Some years ago, ultraviolet spectroscopy would have been the probable selected method for determining residual free styrene monomer in polystryene. However, as shown by

Crompton *et al.*[261] and discussed in Chapter 1, section 10, this technique suffers from several disadvantages. In addition to lack of sensitivity, which limits the lower detection limit to about 200 ppm styrene in polymer under the most favourable circumstances, ultraviolet spectroscopic methods are subject to interference by some of the types of antioxidants included in polystyrene formulations. Such interferences can only be overcome by applying a lengthy pre-treatment of the sample to remove antioxidants prior to spectroscopic analysis.

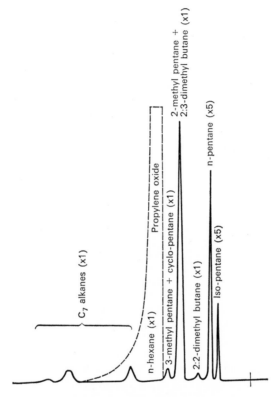

FIG. 68. Gas chromatogram of expanding agents liberated from expandable polystyrene at 200°C for 15 min in helium.[260]

Chromatographed on 10 ft × $\frac{3}{16}$ in. i.d. 25% di-n-butyl phthalate on 44/60 Celite at 40°C and 50 ml/min helium flow, with thermal conductivity detection.

In addition to residual styrene monomer, polystyrene may also contain traces of other aromatic hydrocarbons such as benzene, toluene, xylenes, ethyl benzene and cumene which originate either as impurities in the styrene monomer employed to manufacture the polystyrene or they may have been used in small quantities as dilution solvents at some stage of the manufacturing process. Ultraviolet spectroscopic methods for determining styrene cannot differentiate between the various volatile substances present in polystyrene.

Various workers[263, 264, 265, 279, 280] have studied the application of gas chromatography to the determination of styrene monomer and other aromatic volatile constituents in styrene copolymers, emulsions and lattices. Ragelis and Gajan[266] have described a gas chromato-graphic method for the determination of styrene monomer in polystyrene but do not discuss the determination of other volatiles in the polymer. In this procedure a known weight of polymer is dissolved in benzene and a portion of the solution injected on to a column of diisodecyl phthalate on Chromosorb W support. Argon is used as the carrier gas with an argon ionization detector (with radium source). Pfab and Noffz[267] have described two methods, both based on gas chromatography, for the determination of styrene monomer and other volatiles in polystyrene. In one method an orthodichlorobenzene solution of the polymer is distilled to isolate volatiles as a concentrate in the distillate. The orthodichloro-benzene used to dissolve the polymer contains a known amount of toluene which is used as an internal standard. The distillate is chromatographed on a polyethylene glycol column using helium as a carrier gas and a katharometer detector. This method is claimed to determine styrene and ethyl benzene in polystyrene. In their second method, Pfab and Noffz dissolve the polymer in methylene dichloride containing a known amount of 1-phenyl butane as internal standard. The polymer is then reprecipitated by the addition of excess methyl alcohol. The filtrate is chromatographed as described above, except that a flame ionization detector is used instead of a katharometer in order to increase the overall sensiti-vity of the procedure. This method is claimed to be capable of determining styrene monomer, ethyl benzene, cumene and xylenes.

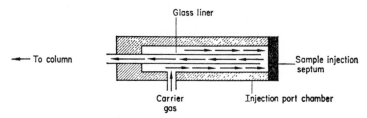

FIG. 69. Injection port glass liner fitted to F. & M. Model 1609 gas chromatograph. The glass liner measures 60 mm × 40 mm o.d. × 2 mm i.d. and is very loosely packed with glass fibre.[262]

Both the Ragelis and Gajan[266] and the Pfab and Noffz[267] gas chromatographic proce-dures have a similar order of sensitivity to the previously discussed ultraviolet spectroscopic procedures (i.e. lower detection limit 200–300 ppm of styrene monomer). More recently, Shapras and Claver[268] have described a gas chromatographic method for the determination of various volatiles in polystyrene, styrene–acrylonitrile copolymers, styrene–acrylonitrile–butadiene terpolymers and other copolymers. In this procedure, the polymer is dissolved in dimethyl formamide containing a known amount of toluene as internal standard. A portion of this solution is injected into two columns in series comprising 20% Tween 81 on Chromosorb W, followed by 10% Resoflex-446 on Chromosorb W. Using a hydrogen flame ionization detector, it is claimed that less than 10 ppm of various monomer and other volatile impurities can be determined in the polymer by this procedure. Shapras and Claver state that the polymer present in the solution injected into the gas chromatographic column deposits on the injection block and is removed by reaming after every fifty sample injections.

Crompton et al.[261, 262] have extended the gas chromatographic technique to the deter-mination in polystyrene of styrene and a wide range of other aromatic volatiles in amounts down to the 10 ppm level. In this method a weighed portion of the sample is dissolved in propylene oxide containing a known concentration of pure n-undecane as an internal standard. After allowing any insolubles to settle an approximately measured volume of the solution is injected into the chromatographic column which contains 10% Chromosorb 15–20 M supported on 60–70 BS Celite. Helium is used as carrier gas and a hydrogen flame ionization detector is employed.

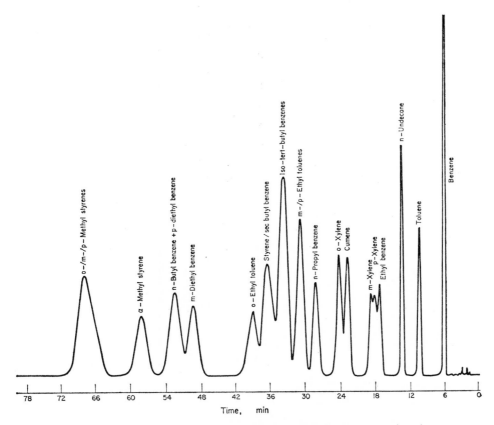

FIG. 70. Gas chromatogram of synthetic blend of hydrocarbons likely to occur in polystyrene on a Carbowax 15–20M column at 80°.[262]

In Fig. 69 is shown a device[262] which is connected to the injection port of the gas chromatograph in order to prevent the deposition of polymeric material in the injection port of the chromatograph with consequent blockages. When a solution of polystyrene is injected into the liner, polymer is retained by the glass fibre and volatile components are swept on to the chromatographic column by the carrier gas.

Figure 70 illustrates, by means of a synthetic mixture, the various aromatics that can be resolved, whilst Fig. 71 illustrates a chromatogram obtained with a polystyrene sample, indicating the presence of benzene, toluene, ethyl benzene, xylenes, cumene, propyl benzenes, ethyl toluenes, butyl benzenes, styrene and α-methyl styrene.[262] This method is described in detail below.

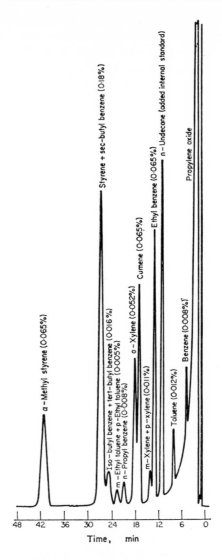

Fig. 71. Analysis of anhydrous propylene
oxide solution of polystyrene for residual
aromatic hydrocarbons—using a Carbowax 15–20M column and glass liner in
injection port. Internal standard n-undecane. Concentrations are expressed as
% w/w in the polymer.[262]

Instrument

F & M Model 1609 (or equivalent) gas chromatograph with hydrogen flame
ionization detector and an injection port fitted with glass liner, very loosely filled
with glass wool (Fig. 69).

Column

Copper tube (15 ft × ¼ in. o.d. × $\frac{3}{16}$ in. i.d.) packed with 10% w/w Carbowax 15–20 M supported on 60–72 B.S. mesh Celite.

Gas pressures and flows

Helium	30 lbf/in² gauge,	100 ml/min
Air	7 lbf/in² gauge,	650 ml/min
Hydrogen	12 lbf/in² gauge,	75 ml/min

Temperatures

Injection	150°C
Detector	150°C
Column	80°C
Flame	200°C

Recorder

Honeywell-Brown, −0·2 to +1·0 mV range, 1 sec response, 15 in.(381 mm)/hr chart speed.

Reagents

Carbowax 15–20 M and 60–72 B.S. mesh Celite from Griffin and George Limited, Wembley, Middlesex. Styrene and propylene oxide from Shell Chemicals U.K. Limited, Carrington, Urmston, Manchester. Ortho-, meta- and para-xylenes, cumene, n-propyl benzene, isobutyl benzene, α-methyl styrene and mixed meta-/para-diethyl benzenes from Kodak Limited, Kirkby, Liverpool. Tert-, sec- and n-butyl benzenes, ortho-methyl styrene, mixed meta-/para-methyl styrenes, and n-undecane from Koch-Light Laboratories Limited, Colnbrook, Buckinghamshire. Meta- and para-ethyl toluenes from B. Newton Maine Limited, North Walsham, Norfolk. Ortho-ethyl toluene from Ralph N. Emmanuel Limited, London.

Analytical procedure

CALIBRATION. Weigh in turn into a 10 ml volumetric flask 1·0 ml n-undecane, 1·0 ml α-methyl styrene, 1·0 ml styrene, 0·5 ml ethyl benzene, 0·5 ml cumene, 0·5 ml n-propyl benzene, 0·25 ml meta- or para-xylene, 0·25 ml ortho-xylene, 0·25 ml meta- or para-ethyl toluene, 0·25 ml toluene and 0·1 ml benzene. Dilute to 10 ml with propylene oxide and then further dilute 0·25 ml of the solution to 25 ml with propylene oxide. If necessary, the aromatic hydrocarbons in the blend may be limited to those it is specifically required to determine. Chromatograph 5 μl of the calibration blend at a range setting of × 10 and suitable attenuation settings. This calibration procedure should be carried out daily.

ANALYSIS. Prepare the polymer solvent by weighing 0·1 ml n-undecane into a 100 ml volumetric flask and then diluting to 100 ml with propylene oxide. Weigh accurately about 1 g polymer into a 25-ml stoppered measuring cylinder, add exactly 10 ml of the prepared polymer solvent from a pipette, seal with a serum cap and shake until the polymer has dissolved. Gel, pigment and filler may remain as an undissolved suspension without detriment to the analysis. Chromatograph 5 microlitre of the solution at a range setting of × 10 and suitable attenuation settings.

F

RELATIVE RETENTION DISTANCES Retention distances (injection point to peak centres) are corrected for the gas hold-up of the column and are expressed relative to styrene:

Benzene	0·17
Toluene	0·29
n-Undecane	0·40
Ethyl benzene	0·47
meta-Xylene	0·50
para-Xylene	0·50
Cumene	0·62
ortho-Xylene	0·66
n-Propyl benzene	0·77
meta-Ethyl toluene	0·84
para-Ethyl toluene	0·84
iso-Butyl benzene	0·92
tert-Butyl benzene	0·92
sec-Butyl benzene	1·00
Styrene	1·00
ortho-Ethyl toluene	1·05
meta-Diethyl benzene	1·35
para-Diethyl benzene	1·44
n-Butyl benzene	1·44
α-Methyl styrene	1·60
ortho-Methyl styrene	1·86
meta-Methyl styrene	1·86
para-Methyl styrene	1·86

CALCULATION On the calibration and analysis chromatograms, measure the peak heights of the n-undecane and the aromatic hydrocarbons allowing for any attenuation factors. From the calibration chromatogram, determine the response fraction for each component as follows:

A = weight of component in calibration blend,
B = weight of n-undecane in calibration blend,
C = peak height of component on calibration chromatograph,
D = peak height of n-undecane on calibration chromatograph.

$$\text{Component response factor, } F = \frac{A}{B} \times \frac{D}{C}$$

From the analysis chromatogram, determine the concentration of each component as follows:

f = component response factor,
g = peak height of component on analysis chromatogram,
h = peak height of n-undecane on analysis chromatogram,
j = % w/w n-undecane in polymer solvent,
k = weight (g) of polymer taken for analysis.

$$\text{Component } \% \text{ w/w} = \frac{10 \times G \times F \times J}{H \times K}$$

Gas chromatography is eminently suitable for the determination of volatile expanding agents present in expanded cellular grades of polystyrene. Normal and isopentane are commonly used for this purpose. The method quoted below enables these and wide range of other volatiles to be determined in polystyrene with a reasonable degree of accuracy.

The sample is chromatographed as a solution in methylene dichloride in the presence of 2:4-dimethyl pentane as an internal standard. The concentrations of the components are determined from peak height ratios and response factors.

OPERATING CONDITIONS

Instrument:	F & M Model 1609 or equivalent instrument with injection liner (see Fig. 69).
Column:	Copper tube (10 ft × $\frac{1}{4}$ in. o.d. × $\frac{3}{16}$ in. i.d.) packed with 25% w/w di-n-butyl phthalate on 44–60 Celite.
Gases: Helium	30 psig, rotameter at 4·0
Air	10 psig, rotameter at 2·0
Hydrogen	$7\frac{1}{2}$ psig, rotameter at 3·0
Temperatures:	°C
Injection	165
Column	50
Detector	125
Flame	170
Recorder:	1 mV, 24 in./hr.

To a 100 ml volumetric flask add 95 ml of a suitable solvent. Seal with a serum cap and weigh. Through the serum cap, add in turn 0·25 ml methyl cyclopentane, 1 ml 2:4-dimethyl pentane, 0·25 ml n-hexane, 0·5 ml 3-methyl pentane, 1 ml 2-methyl pentane, 0·5 ml 2:2-dimethyl butane, 0·5 ml n-pentane and 0·5 ml iso-pentane, re-weighing after each addition. Include in this calibration mixture only those substances it is required to determine in the polystyrene sample. Chromatograph 5 μl at a range of × 100 and suitable attenuations.

Weigh 1 g polymer sample into a 25 ml measuring cylinder, add 10 ml of a 1% v/v solution of 2:4-dimethyl butane in solvent (internal standard, see Note 2), seal with a serum cap and shake to dissolve. Chromatograph 5 μl at a range of × 100 and suitable attenuations.

Measure the peak heights of all the components, allowing for any attenuation factors, on both the calibration and analysis chromatograms.

From the calibration chromatogram, calculate response factors as follows:

P = peak height of component,

H = peak height of 2:4-dimethyl pentane,

A = weight of component in calibration mixture,

B = weight of 2:4-dimethyl pentane in calibration mixture.

$$\text{Response factor, } F = \frac{A}{B} \times \frac{H}{P}$$

From the analysis chromatogram, calculate the concentration of each component as follows:

$W = \%$ w/w 2:4-dimethyl pentane in solvent,

$S = $ weight of sample taken,

$C = $ peak height of component,

$D = $ peak height of 2:4-dimethyl pentane,

$F = $ response factor for component.

$$\text{Component } (\% \text{ w/w}) = \frac{C}{D} \times \frac{10 \times W}{S} \times F.$$

The following are uncorrected retention distances (injection point to peak apex) and the corresponding relative values (2:4-dimethyl pentane $= 1\cdot00$).

Component	DR	
	mm	rel.
Isopentane	$21\frac{1}{2}$	0·30
n-Pentane	$25\frac{1}{2}$	0·36
2:2-Dimethyl butane	$33\frac{1}{2}$	0·46
2-Methyl pentane + 2:3-dimethyl butane	44	0·61
3-Methyl pentane + cyclopentane	$50\frac{1}{2}$	0·70
n-Hexane	$57\frac{1}{2}$	0·80
2:4-Dimethyl pentane	72	1·00
Methyl cyclopentane	$84\frac{1}{2}$	1·17

Note 1. The following solvents are recommended:

Present in sample	Solvent
n-pentane	propylene oxide
isopentane	
2:2-dimethyl butane	
isobutane	
cyclopentane	methylene dichloride
isopentane	
n-pentane	
2:2-dimethyl butane	
2-methyl pentane	
2:3-dimethyl butane	
3-methyl pentane	
cyclopentane	
n-hexane	
2:4-dimethyl pentane	
methyl cyclopentane	
iso-octane	benzene

Note 2. The following internal standards are recommended when paraffins up to C_5 only are present in the polymer.

Present in sample	*Internal standard*
isobutane and/or 2:2-dimethyl butane	n-pentane
n- and/or isopentane	2:2-dimethyl butane
iso-octane	methyl cyclopentane

Shapras and Claver[290] describe the determination of residual monomers, non-polymerizable polymer volatiles and additives in styrene based resins by a procedure involving chromatography of a solution or dispersion of the sample in dimethyl formamide on a tandem column made up of 3 ft of 20% Tween 81 followed by 10 ft of 10% Resoflex 446 at a column temperature of 120°C. Stevens[291] describes the determination of acrolein and furfural monomers in phenol/acrolein and phenol/furfural resins and also[292] the determination of phenol and formaldehyde in phenol formaldehyde resins. Phenol is estimated on a silicone SF-96 column, using *m*-cresol as internal standard, whilst formaldehyde is estimated on a sucrose octa-acetate column, using n-butanol as the internal standard. Priori and Panetti[307] describe the determination of free phenol, cresols and xylenols in phenoplasts by first separating the phenolics chemically and then completing the analysis gas chromatographically on a silicone oil column.

Gas chromatography has been successfully applied to the determination of monomers other than styrene and other types of volatiles in various types of polymers, and rubbers. Cobler and Samsel[281] mention the determination of residual monomers in polymers. Tweet and Miller[264] determined monomers in ethyl acrylate/styrene copolymer emulsions by distilling off the monomers in the presence of toluene and then examining on a silicone grease column using toluene as the internal standard.

Brodsky[282] and Nelson *et al.*[283] discuss the determination of monomers, including styrene, in latex samples. These procedures involve the direct injection of the latex into the gas chromatographic column.

Haslam *et al.*[284, 286, 287] identified mixed solvents, and impurities in plastics and in plastic adhesives [287, 288] by a combination of gas chromatography and infrared spectroscopy, and chemical analysis.

REFERENCES

1. ZIJP, J. W. H., *Rubber Chem. & Technol.* **30**, 705 (1957).
2. WADELIN, C. W., *Anal. Chem.* **28**, 1530 (1956).
3. NEWELL, J. E. and PASAIC, N. J., U.S. Rubber Co. General Laboratories, unpublished paper (1952).
4. NAWAKAWSKI, A. C., *Anal. Chem.* **30**, 1868 (1958).
5. HILTON, C. L., *Anal. Chem.* **32**, 383 (1960).
6. SPELL, H. L. and EDDY, R. D., *Anal. Chem.* **32**, 1811 (1960).
7. WEXLER, A. S., *Anal. Chem.* **35**, 1926 (1963).
8. METCALF, K. and TOMLINSON, R. F., *Plastics* **25**, 319 (1960).
9. MORGENTHALER, L. P., Unpublished work.
10. British Standard 2782, Part 4, Method 405D (1965).
11. STAFFORD, C., *Anal. Chem.* **34**, 794 (1962).
12. BERGER, K. G., SYLVESTER, N. D. and HAINES, D. M., *Analyst* **85**, 341 (1960).
13. MAYER, H., *Deut. Lebensm. Rundschau* **57**, 170 (1961).
14. GLAVIND, J., *Acta Chem. Scand.* **17**, 1635 (1963).
15. BLOIS, M. S., *Nature* **181**, 1199 (1958).
16. CROMPTON, T. R., *European Polymer Journal* **4**, 473 (1968).
17. LORENZ, O., SCHEELE, W. and DUMMER, W., *Kautschuk Gummi* **7**, WT, 273 (1954).
18. LUONGO, J. P., *Appl. Spectroscopy* **19**, (4), 117 (1965).
19. MILLER, R. G. J. and WILLIS, H. A., *Spectrochim. Acta* **14**, 119 (1959).
20. GUICHON, G. and HENNIKER, J., *British Plastics* **37**, 74 (1964).
21. DRUSHEL, H. V. and SOMMERS, A. L., *Anal. Chem.* **36**, 836 (1964).
22. WHEELER, D. A., *Talanta* **15**, 1315 (1968).
23. CAMPBELL, R. H. and WISE, R. W., *J. Chromatography.* **12**, 178 (1963).
24. SLONAKER, D. F. and SIEVERS, D. C., *Anal. Chem.* **36**, 1130 (1964).
25. VAN DER HEIDE, R. F. and WOUTERS, O., *Z. Lebensm. Untersuch Forsch.* **117**, 129 (1962).
26. SCHRÖDER, E. and RUDOLPH, G., *Plaste Kautschuk* **10**, 22 (1963).
27. METCALF, K. and TOMLINSON, R., *Plastics (London)* **25**, 319 (1960).
28. WOGGON, H., KORN, O. and JEHLE, D., *Die Nahrung* **9**, 495 (1965).
29. British Standard 2782, Part 4, Method 405D (1965).
30. Ibid., Method 405B (1965).
31. YUSHKEVICHYUTE, S. S. and SHLYAPNIKOV, YU. A., *Plasticheskie Massy*, No. 1, 54 (1967).
32. SPELL, H. L. and EDDY, R. D., *Anal. Chem.* **32**, 1811 (1960).
33. STAFFORD, C., *ibid.* **34**, 794 (1962).
34. KORN, O. and WOGGON, H., *Plaste Kautschuk* **11**, 278 (1964).
35. ZILIO-GRANDI, F., LIBRALESSO, G., SASSU, G. and SVEGLIDAO, G., *Mater. Plast. Elast.* **30**, 643 (1964).
36. BROCK, M. J. and LOUTH, G. D., *Anal. Chem.* **27**, 1575 (1955).
37. WANDEL, M. and TENGLER, H., *Fette Seifen, Anstrichmittel* **66**, 815 (1964).
38. VARMA, J. P., SURYANARAYA, N. P. and SIRCAR, A. K., *J. Sci. Ind. Res. India* **20**, 79 (1961).
39. YUASA, T. and KAMIYA, K., *Japan Analyst* **13**, 966 (1964).
40. VARMA, J. P., SURYANARAYA, N. P. and SIRCAR, A. L., *J. Sci. Ind. Res. India* **21**, 49 (1962).
41. HILTON, C. L., *Anal. Chem.* **32**, 1554 (1960).
42. MYERS, A. W., ROGERS, C. E., STANNETT, V. and SZWARC, M., *Mod. Plastics* **34**, 157 (1957).
43. KLUTE, C. H. and FRANKLIN, P. J., *J. Polymer Science* **32**, 161 (1958).
44. CROMPTON, T. R., *J. Appl. Polymer Sci.* **6**, 538 (1962).
45. BRANDT, H. J., *Anal. Chem.* **33**, 1390 (1960).
46. CORNISH, P. J., *J. Appl. Polymer Sci.* **7**, 727 (1963).
47. YUSHKEVICHYUTE, S. S. and SHLYAPNIKOV, YU. A., *Plasticheskie Massy*, No. 12, 62 (1966).
48. SCHEELE, W., GRASEMANN, H. and MAY, G., *Kautschuk Gummi* **16**, WT 241 (1957).

49. SCHEELE, W., MAU, G. and KEMME G., *Kautschuk Gummi* **13,** WT 33 (1959).
50. MURAKAMI, S., FUKUMORI, T., TSURUGI, J. and MURATA, N. *J. Chem. Soc. Japan, Ind. Chem. Sect.* **67,** 1161 (1964).
51. MOCKER, F., *Kautschuk Gummi* **11,** WT 281 (1958).
52. Idem, *ibid.* **12,** WT 155 (1959).
53. Idem, *ibid.* **13,** WT 91 (1960).
54. MOCKER, F. and OLD, J., *ibid.* **12,** WT 190 (1959).
55. ADAMS, R. N., *Rev. Polarog.* **11,** 71 (1963).
56. ZWEIG, A., LANCASTER, E., NEGLIA, M. T. and JURA, W. H., *J. Am. Chem. Soc.* **86,** 413 (1964).
57. VODZINSKII, YU. and SEMCHIKOVA, G. S., *T. po Khim. i Khim. Teknol.* 272 (1963).
58. VERMILLION, F. J. and PEARL, T. A., *J. Electrochem. Soc.* **111,** 1392 (1964).
59. BARENDRECHT, E., *Anal. Chim. Acta* **24,** 498 (1961).
60. GAYLOR, V. F., ELVING, P. J. and CONRAD, A. L., *Anal. Chem.* **25,** 1078 (1953).
61. HEDENBURG, J. F. and FREISER, H., *Anal. Chem.* **25,** 1355 (1953).
62. WARD, G. A., *Talanta* **10,** 261 (1963).
63. Analytical Applications Report No. 637D, Southern Analytical Ltd., Camberley, Surrey, England.
64. Analytical Applications Report No. 651/2, Southern Analytical Ltd., Camberley, Surrey, England.
65. BUDKE, C., BANNERJEE, D. K. and MILLER, F. D., *Anal. Chem.* **36,** 523 (1964).
66. HAMILTON, J. W. and TAPPEL, A. L., *J. Am. Oil Chemists Soc.* **40,** 52 (1963).
67. LINTNER, C. J., SCHLEIF, R. H. and HIGUCHI, T., *Anal. Chem.* **22,** 534 (1950).
68. HILTON, C. L., *Rubber Age* **84,** 263 (1958).
69. SAWADA, M., YAMAJI and YAMASHINA, T., *J. Soc. Rubber Ind. (Japan)* **35,** 284 (1962).
70. DAVIES, J. R., *Analyst* **90,** 216 (1965).
71. LORENZ, O. and PARKS, C. R., *Anal. Chem.* **34,** 394 (1962).
72. ROBERTSON, M. W. and ROWLEY, R. M. *British Plastics*, January 26 (1960).
73. HASLAM, J. and SOPPET, W. W., *J. Soc. Chem.* **67,** 33 (1948).
74. DOEHRING, H., *Kunststoffe* **28,** 230 (1938).
75. THINIUS, K., *Analytische Chemie der Plaste*, Springer, Berlin, 1952.
76. HASLAM, J. and SQUIRRELL, D. C. M., *Analyst* **80,** 871 (1955).
77. WAKE, W. C., *The Analysis of Rubber and Rubber-like Polymers*, MacLaren, London, 1958.
78. CLARKE, A. D. and BAZILL, G., *British Plastics*, **31,** 16 (1958).
79. BECKER, H. A., *J. Appl. Polymer Sci.* **1,** 212 (1959).
80. GUICHON, G. and HENNIKER, J., *British Plastics*, February (1964), 74.
81. CRIDDLE, W. J., *British Plastics*, May (1963), 242.
82. CACHIA, M., SOUTHWART, D. W. and DAVISON, W. H. T., *J. Appl. Chem.* **8,** 291 (1958).
83. NAWAKOWSKI, A. C., *Anal. Chem.* **30,** 1868 (1958).
84. BRANDT, H. J., *Anal. Chem.* **33,** 1390 (1961).
85. KUTA, E. J. and QUACKENBUSH, F. W., *Anal. Chem.* **32,** 1069 (1960).
86. BUKATA, S. W., ZABROCKI, L. L. and McLAUGHLIN, M. F., *Anal. Chem.* **35,** 886 (1963).
87. BRAMMER, J. A., FROST, S. and REID, V. W., *Analyst* **92,** 91 (1967).
88. PURDY, S. J. and TRUTER, E. V., *Laboratory Practice*, June (1964) 500.
89. KIRCHNER, J. G., MILLER, J. M. and RICE, R. G., *J. Agric. Food Chem.* **2,** 1031 (1954).
90. STANLEY, W. L., VANNIER, S. H. and GENTILI, B., *J. Assoc. Offic. Agric. Chem.* **40,** 282 (1957).
91. SCHEMMER, F. and LINK, E., *Pharm. Ztg.* **104,** 1349 (1959).
92. GÄNSHIRT, H. and MORIANZ, K., *Arch. Pharm.* **293,** 1065 (1960).
93. HEFENDEHL, F. W., *Planta Medica* **8,** 65 (1960).
94. SEHER, A., *Die Nahrung* **4,** 466 (1960).
95. PURDY, S. J. and TRUTER, E. V., *Analyst* **87,** 802 (1962).
96. ATTAWAY, J. A., WALFORD, R. W. and EDWARDS, G. J., *Anal. Chem.* **37,** 74 (1965).
97. PEIFER, J. J., *Mikrokim. Acta* **34** (1962/63).
98. WAGGON, H., KORN, O. and JEHLE, D., *Die Nahrung* **4,** 495 (1965).
99. CAMPBELL, R. H. and WIZE, R. W., *J. Chromatography* **12,** 178 (1963).
100. FIORENZA, A., BONOMI, G. and SEREDI, A., *Mater. Plast. Elast.* **31,** or **10,** 1045 (1965).
101. PARKER, C. A., *J. Roy. Inst. Chem.* **81,** 674 (1957).
102. SEDLÁČEK, B. A. J., *Fette Seifen, Anstrichmittel* **65,** 915 (1963).
103. ROY, B. R., MITRA, S. N. and SEN GUPTA, P. N., *Current Sci. (India)* **29,** 132 (1960).
104. DELVES, R. B., *J. Inst. Petrol.* **48,** 283 (1962).
105. POSPÍŠIL, J. and TAIMR, L., *Collection Czech. Commun.* **30,** 1513 (1965).
106. WILLIAMSON, F. B., *Rubber J. Intern. Plastics*, **148** (No. 2), 24 (1966).
107. ZIJP, J. W. H., *Rec. Trav. Chim.* **75,** 1155 (1956).
108. Idem, Dissertia, Technical University, Delft (1955).
109. AULER, H., *Gummi Asbest Kunststoffe*, **14,** 1024 (1961).
110. BIEFER, K. E., *Mitt. Gebiete Lebensm. Hyg.* **53,** 243 (1952).

111. ZIJP, J. W. H., *Rec. Trav. Chim.* **75**, 1129 (1956).
112. KABOTE, T., KUTIBAYASHI, S. and FURUHAMA, T., *J. Soc. Rubber Ind. (Japan)* **35**, 669 (1962).
113. MIKSCH, R. and PRÖLSS, L., *Gummi Asbest Kunststoffe* **13**, 250 (1960).
114. AULER, H., *Rubber Chem. Technol.* **37**, 950 (1964).
115. BELLAMY, L. J., LAWRIE, J. H. and PREN, E. W. S., *Trans. Inst. Rubber Industry* **15** (1947).
116. MANN, J., *Trans. Inst. Rubber Industry* **27**, 232 (1951).
117. PARKER, C. A. and BERRIMAN, J. M., *Trans. Rubber Industry* **28**, 279 (1952).
118. BUDIG, K. H., *Kautschuk Gummi* **4**, 278 (1951).
119. KUL'BERG, L. M. and BLOKH, G. A., *Zavodskaya Lab.* **14**, 278 (1948).
120. MORRISON, G. D. and SHEPHERD, T., *Trans. Inst. Rubber Industry* **22**, 189 (1946).
121. BURMISTROV, S. I., *Zavodskaya Lab.* **14**, 787 (1948).
122. SCHAEFER, W., *Kautschuk Gummi* **1**, 149 (1948); *Rubber Chem. and Technol.* **23**, 292 (1950).
123. SCHAEFER, W., *Gummi-Ztg* **55**, 400 (1941); *India-Rubber J.* **105**, 303 (1943).
124. SHIMADA, K., *India-Rubber J.* **96**, 380, 415, 446 (1938); *J. Soc. Chem. Ind. (Japan)* **36**, 82, 260, 262 (1933).
125. SLEPUSCHKINA, E. P., *ibid.* **95**, 290 (1938).
126. ENDOH, H., *J. Soc. Chem. Ind. (Japan)* **39**, 11, 12, 52, 146 (1936); **38**, 618 (1935).
127. DEAL, A. J. A., *Trans. Inst. Rubber Industry* **23**, 148 (1947).
128. BURCHFIELD, H. P. and JUDY, J. N., *Anal. Chem.* **19**, 786 (1947).
129. KOBOZEV, M. M., *Lab. Prakt. (U.S.S.R.)* **16**, No. 6, 29 (1941).
130. CRAIG, D., *Ind. Eng. Chem. (Anal. Ed.)* **9**, 56 (1937).
131. KIRCHOF, F. *Kautschuk* **7**, 7 (1931).
132. BELLAMY, L. J., LAWRIE, J. H. and PRESS, E. W. S., *Trans. Inst. Rubber Industry* **22**, 308 (1947); **23**, 15 (1947)
133. DAVIES, D. S., GOLDSMITH, H. S., GUPTA, A. K. and LESTER, G. R., *J. Chem. Soc.* **4926** (1956).
134. SEDLACEK, B., *Vopr Pitaniya* **23**, 8 (1964).
135. STANLEY, W. L., VANNIER, S. H. and GENTILI, B., *Association of Official Agricultural Chemists* **40**, 282 (1957).
136. VIOQUE, E. and HOLMAN, R. T., *American Oil Chemists Soc. Journal* **39**, 63 (1962).
137. DELVES, R. B., *J. Institute of Petroleum* **48**, 283 (1962).
138. LE ROSEN, A. L. *et al.*, *Anal. Chem.* **22**, 809 (1950).
139. PEURIFLOY, P. V. and NAGER, M., *Anal. Chem.* **32**, 1135 (1960).
140. BOBBITT, J. M., *Thin-Layer Chromatography*, New York, Reinhold Publishing Corporation (1963).
141. DAHN, H. and FUCHS, H., *Helv. Chim. Acta* **45**, 261 (1962).
142. DORFNER, K., *Ionenaustauscher*, Berlin, Walter de Gruyter & Co. (1963).
143. HAIS, I. M. and MACEK, K., *Handbuch der Papier-chromatographie*, Bd. I. Jena, VEB Gustav Fisher Verlag (1958).
144. HALPAAP, H., *Chem.-Ing. Tech.* **35**, 488 (1963).
145. HONEGGER, C. G., *Helv. Chim. Acta* **45**, 1409 (1962).
146. HONEGGER, C. G., *Helv. Chim. Acta* **46**, 1772 (1963).
147. MUNTER, F. *Chem. Ztg.* **87**, 657 (1963).
148. PATAKI, G. and KELLER, M., *Helv. Chim. Acta* **46**, 1054 (1963).
149. PEEREBOOM, J. W. C., *J. Chromatography* **4**, 323 (1960).
150. RANDERATH, K., *Dünnschicht-Chromatographie*, Weinheim Verlag Chemie GmbH, English edit. New York, Academic Press (1963).
151. RITTER, F. J. and MEYER, G. M., *Nature (London)* **193**, 941 (1962).
152. SCHULZE, P. E. and WENZEL, M., *Angew. Chem.* **74**, 777 (1962).
153. STAHL, E., *Chem. Ztg.* **82**, 323 (1959).
154. STAHL, E., *Arch. Pharmaz.* **291**, 411 (1959).
155. STAHL, E., *Dünnschicht-Chromatographie, ein Laboratoriums-Handbuch*, Berlin-Göttingen-Heidelberg, Springer Verlag, English edit. New York, Academic Press (1964).
156. TRUTER, E. V., *Thin Film Chromatography*, London, Cleaver-Hume Press Ltd. (1963).
157. TSCHESCHE, R., BIERNOTH, G. and WULFF, G., *J. Chromatography* **12**, 342 (1963).
158. WALDI, D., In Stahl, E. ref. 155.
159. ZECHMEISTER, L. and VON CHOLNOKY, L., *Die chromatographische Adsorptions-analyse*, 2 Aufl. Wien, Springer-Verlag (1938).
160. DOHMANN, K., *Laboratory Practice*, July (1965).
161. STAHL, E., *Laboratory Practice*, June (1964).
162. HALPAAP, H., *Chem.-Ing. Techn.* **35**, 488 (1963).
163. SLONAKER, D. F. and SIEVERS, D. C., *Anal. Chem.* **36**, 1130 (1964).
164. KIRCHNER, J. G., MILLER, J. M. and RICE, T. G., *J. Agr. Food Chem.* **2**, 1031 (1954).
165. SEHER, A., *Fette Seifen, Anstrichmittel* **61**, 345 (1959).
166. VAN DER HEIDE, R. F., MAAGDENBERG, A. C. and VAN DER NEUT, J. H., *Chem. Weekblad* **61**, 440 (1965).
167. VAN DER NEUT, J. H. and MAAGDENBERG, A. C., *Plastics (London)* **31**, 66 (1965).

168. NEUBERT, G., *Z. Anal. Chem.* **203**, 265 (1964).
169. VAN DER HEIDE, R. F., *Z. Lebensm. Untersuch. Forsch.* **124**, 198 (1964).
170. DAVIDEK, J. and POKORNÝ, J., *Rev. Univ. Ind. Santander* **4**, 11 (1962).
171. ISHIKAWA, S. and KATSUN, G., *Bitamin* **30**, 203 (1964).
172. DAVIDEK, J. and POKORNÝ, J., *Z. Lebensm. Untersuch. Forsch.* **115**, 113 (1961).
173. MATTHEWS, T. V. and MITRA, S. N., *Indian J. Technol.* **3**, 102 (1965).
174. COPIUS-PEEVEBOOM, J. W., *Nature* **204**, 748 (1964).
175. COOK, C. D., NASH, N. G. and FLANAGAN, H. R., *J. Am. Chem. Soc.* **75**, 6242 (1953).
176. SEHER, A., *Fette Seifen, Anstrichmittel* **61**, 345 (1959).
177. VAN DER NEUT, J. H. and MAAGDENBERG, A. C., *Plastics*, Jan. (1966) 66.
178. VAN DER HEIDE, R. F. and WOUTERS, O., *Z. für Lebensmittelforschung* **17**, 129 (1962).
179. WAGGON, H. and JEHLE, D., *Die Nahrung* **4**, 495 (1965).
180. BRAUN, D., *Chimica Ind.* **19**, 77 (1965).
181. WANDEL, M., and TENGLER, H., *Kunststoffe* **55**, 11 (1965).
182. HAALPAAP, H., *Chem. Ing. Tech.* **35**, 488 (1963).
183. KNAPPE, E. and PETERI, D., *Z. Analyt. Chem.* **188**, 184 (1961).
184. LYNES, A., *J. Chromatography* **15**, 108 (1964).
185. LANE, E. S., *J. Chromatography* **18**, 426 (1965).
186. BRAUN, D. and GEENEN, H., *J. Chromatography* **7**, 56 (1962).
187. CRUMP, G. B., *Anal. Chem.* **36**, 2447 (1964).
188. DENTI, E. and LUBOZ, M. P., *J. Chromatography* **18**, 325 (1965).
189. DALLAS, M. S. J., *J. Chromatography* **17**, 267 (1965).
190. BARK, L. S., GRAHAM, R. J. T. and McCORMICK, *Talanta* **12**, 122 (1965).
191. SHELLARD, E. J., *Lab. Pract.* **13**, 290 (1964).
192. MILLET, M. A., MOORE, W. E. and SAEMAN, J. F., *Anal. Chem.* **36**, 491 (1964).
193. BROWN. T. L. and BENJAMIN, J., *Anal. Chem.* **36**, 446 (1964).
194. ROBERTS, C. B. and SWARK, J. D., *Anal. Chem.* **36**, 271 (1964).
195. SCHRODER, E. and RUDOLF, G., *Plaste und Kautschuk* **1**, 22 (1963).
196. GUICHON, G., and HENNIKER, J., *British Plastics* **37**, 74 (1964).
197. DUVALL, A. H., and TULLY, W. F., *J. Chromatography* **11**, 38 (1963).
198. BROOKS, V. T., *Chemy. Ind.* 1317 (1959).
199. SACHIYUKI, T., *Bunseki Kagaku* **12**, 137 (1963); Lowry Abstract Card 37 6–15–63.
200. PORCARO, P. J., *Anal. Chem.* **36**, 1664 (1964).
201. GRANT, D. W., and VAUGHAN, G. A., in *Gas Chromatography*, p. 305. Edited by M. van Swaay, Butterworths, London (1962).
202. FREEDMAN, R. W. and CHARLIER, G. O., *Anal. Chem.* **36**, 1880 (1964).
203. BUKATA, S. W., ZABROCKI, L. L. and McLAUGHLIN, M. F., *Anal. Chem.* **35**, 885 (1963).
204. HYDEN, S., *Anal. Chem.* **35**, 113 (1963).
205. ABRAHAM, M. H., DAVIES, A. G., LLEWELLYN, D. R., and THAIN, E. M., *Anal. Chim. Acta* **17**, 499 (1957).
206. ESPOSITO, C. G., and SWANN, M. H., *Anal. Chem.* **34**, 1048 (1962).
207. ESPOSITO, C. G., and SWANN, M. H., *Anal. Chem.* **33**, 1854 (1961).
208. ESPOSITO, C. G., *Anal. Chem.* **34**, 1173 (1962).
209. ESPOSITO, C. G., *Anal. Chem.* **35**, 1439 (1963).
210. ZULAICKA, J., and GUICHON, G., *Anal. Chem.* **35**, 1724 (1963).
211. KITUCHI, Y., *Kagaku No. Ryoiki Zokan* **44**, 169 (1961).
212. COOK, C. D., ELGOOD, N. J., SHAW, C. G. and SOLOMON, D .H., *Anal. Chem.* **34**, 1177 (1962).
213. COURTIER, J. C., *Plastiques Modernes et Elastomer*, August–September 132 (1965).
214. GILLIO-TOS, M., and VINIERCATI, A., *Kunststoffe* **56**, 409 (1966).
215. WIZE, R. W. and SULLIVAN, A. B., *Rubber Chemistry and Technology* **35**, No. 3, July–September (1962).
216. KNIGHT, H. S. and SIEGEL, H., *Anal. Chem.* **38**, 1221 (1966).
217. SCHRÖDER, E. and RUDLPH, G., *Plaste Kautschuk* **1**, 22 (1963).
218. ANDERSON, D. M. W., *Analyst* **84**, 50 (1959).
219. GRANT, D. W. and VAUGHAN, G. H., *Gas Chromatography*, p. 305, Butterworths, London (1962).
220. LONG, R. E. and GUVERNATOR, G. C., *Anal. Chem.* **39**, 1493 (1967).
221. NOSIKOV, YU. D. and VETCHINKINA, V. N., *Neftekhimiya* **5**, 284 (1965).
222. HELF, C. and BOCKWAN, D., *Plaste Kautschuk* **11**, 624 (1964).
223. HASLAM, J., SOPPET, W. and WILLIS, H. A., *J. Appl. Chem.* **1**, 112 (1951).
224. LIBERTI, A., COSTA, G. and PAULUZZI, E., *Chim. é Ind.* **38**, 674 (1956).
225. KENDALL, D. N., *Appl. Spectroscopy* **7**, 179 (1953).
226. CACHIA, M., SOUTHWART, D. W. and DAVISON, W. H. T., *J. Appl. Chem.* **8**, 291 (1958).
227. BELLAMY, L. J. and WILLIAMS, R. L., Paper presented at International Symposium on Microchemistry, Birmingham, August (1958).

228. HASLAM, J., JEFFS, A. R. and WILLIS, H. A., *Analyst* **86**, 44 (1961).
229. WHITE, J. U., ALPERT, N. L., WARD, N. M. and GALLAWAY, W. S., *Anal. Chem.* **31**, 1267 (1959).
230. GRASSELLI, J. G and SNAVELY, M. K., *Appl. Spectroscopy* **16**, 190 (1962).
231. BLAKE, B. H., ERLEY, D. S. and BEMAN, F. L., *Appl. Spectroscopy* **18**, 114 (1964).
232. SLOANE, H. J., JOHNS, T., ULRICH, W. F. and CADMAN, W. J., *J. Appl. Spectroscopy* **19**, 130 (1965).
233. ANDERSON, D. M. W., *Analyst* **84**, 994 (1959).
237. CHANG, S. S., IRELAND, C. E. and TAI, H., *Anal. Chem.* **33**, 479 (1961).
239. DAVIDSON, W. H. T., *J. Optical Soc. Am.* **45**, 227 (1955).
240. EGGERTSON, F. T. and GROENNINGS, S., *Anal. Chem.* **30**, 20 (1958).
242. GALLAWAY, W. S., JOHNS, T., TIPOTSCH, D. G. and ULRICH, W. F., Pittsburg Conference on Analytical Chemistry and Applied Spectroscopy, March (1958).
245. HASLAM. J., JEFFS. A. R. and WILLIS, H. A., *Analyst* **86**, 1018 (1961).
248. KUELEMAUS, A. I. M. and KWANTES, A., 4th World Petroleum Congress, Rome (1955).
249. LEGGEN, H. W., *Anal. Chem.* **33**, 1295 (1961).
250. LESSER, J. M., *Anal. Chem.* **31**, 484 (1959).
251. MARTIN, A. J. P., 1st International Gas Chromatographic Symposium, Instrument Society of America, Michigan State University (1957).
252. MOLNAR, W. S. and YARBOROUGH, V. A., *Appl. Spectroscopy* **12**, 143 (1958).
253. SENN, W. L. and DRUSHEL, H. V., *Anal. Chim. Acta* **25**, 328 (1961).
254. SIMMONS, M. C. and KELLEY, T. R., 2nd International Gas Chromatographic Symposium, Instrument Society of America, Michigan State University (1959).
255. SPARAGANA, M. and MASON, W. B., *Anal. Chem.* **34**, 242 (1962).
257. THOMPSON, A. E., *J. Chromatography* **6**, 454 (1961).
258. WHITE, J. U., ALPERT, N. L., WARD, W. M. and GALLAWAY, W. S., *Anal. Chem.* **31**, 1267 (1959).
259. WHITE, J. U., WEINER, S., ALPERT, N. L. and WARD, W. M., *Anal. Chem.* **30**, 1694 (1958).
260. CROMPTON, T. R. and MYERS, L. W., *Plastics and Polymers*, **205**, June 1968.
261. CROMPTON, T. R., MYERS, L. W. and BLAIR, D., *British Plastics*, December 1965.
262. CROMPTON, T. R. and MYERS, L. W., *European Polymer Journal* **4**, 355 (1968).
263. SHAPRAS, P. and CLAVER, G. C., *Anal. Chem.* **34**, 433 (1962).
264. TWEET, O. and MILLER, W. K., *Anal. Chem.* **35**, 852 (1963).
265. WILKINSON, L. B., NORMAN, C. W. and BUETTNER, J. P., *Anal. Chem.* **36**, 1759 (1964).
266. RAGELIS, E. P. and GAJAN, R. J. F., *Assoc. Official Agric. Chem.* **45**, 918 (1962).
267. PFAB, W. and NOFFZ, D., *Z. Anal. Chem.* **195**, 37 (1963).
268. SHAPRAS, P. and CLAVER, G. C., *Anal. Chem.* **36**, 2282 (1964).
269. MINO, G. J., *Polymer Sci.* **22**, 369 (1956).
270. CLAVER, G. C. and MURPHY, M. E., *Anal. Chem.* **31**, 1682 (1959).
271. CROMPTON, T. R. and BUCKLEY, D., *Analyst* **90**, 76 (1965).
272. NASH, R. A., SKAUEN, D. M. and PURDY, W. C., *J. Am. Pharmaceutical Association, Scientific Edition*, **XLVII**, No. 6, 436 (1958)
273. ELVING, P. J. and KRIVIS, A. F., *Anal. Chem.* **30**, 1645 (1958).
274. ELVING, P. J. and KRIVIS, A. F., *Anal. Chem.* **30**, 1648 (1958).
275. GAYLOR, V. F., CONRAD, A. L. and LANDERL, J. H., *Anal. Chem.* **29**, 228 (1957).
276. LORD, S., and ROGERS, L. B., *Anal. Chem.* **26**, 284 (1954).
277. MORRIS, J. B., and SCHEMPF, J. M., *Anal. Chem.* **31**, 286 (1959).
278. GAYLOR, V. F., CONRAD, A. F. and LANDERL, J. H., *Anal. Chem.* **29**, 224 (1957).
279. NOWAK, P. and KLEMMTT, *Kunststoffe* **52**, 604 (1962).
280. ADCOCK, L. H., *Patra J.* **3**, 5 (1962).
281. COBLER, J. G. and SAMSEL, E. P., *Soc. Plast. Eng. Trans.* **2**, 145 (1962).
282. BRODSKY, J., *Kunststoffe* **51**, 20 (1961).
283. NELSON, F. M., EGGERTSEN, F. T. and HOLST, J. J., *Anal. Chem.* **33**, 1150 (1961).
284. HASLAM, T., JEFFS, A. R. and WILLIS, H. A., *J. Oil & Col. Chem. Assoc.* **45**, 325 (1962).
285. ESPOSITO, C. G. and SWANN, H. M., *Anal. Chem.* **33**, 1854 (1961).
286. HASLAM, J., *Chem. Age* **82**, 169 (1959).
287. HASLAM, J. and JEFFS, A. R., *J. Appl. Chem.* **7**, 24 (1957) .
288. HASLAM, J. and JEFFS, A. R., *Analyst* **83**, 455 (1958).
289. HASLAM, J., HAMILTON, J. B., and JEFFS, A. R., *Analyst* **83**, 66 (1958).
290. SHAPRAS, P. and CLAVER, G. C., *Anal. Chem.* **36**, 2282 (1964).
291. STEVENS, M. P., *Anal. Chem.* **37**, 167 (1965).
292. STEVENS, M. P. and PERCIVAL, D. F., *Anal. Chem.* **36**, 1023 (1964).
293. ROBERTS, C. B. and SWANK, J. D., *Anal. Chem.* **36**, 271 (1964).
294. ZULAICKA, J. and GUICHON, G., *Compt. Rend.* **255**, 524 (1962).
295. ZULAICKA, J. and GUICHON, G., *Revista de Plasticos Modernos* **13**, 13 (1963).
296. ZULAICKA, J., LANDAULT, C. and GUICHON, G., *Bull. Soc. Chim. France* 1294 (1962).

297. GUICHON, G. and HENNIKER, J., *British Plastics* **37,** 74 (1964).
298. ZULAICKA, J. and GUICHON, G., *Anal. Chem.* **35,** 1724 (1963).
299. ESPOSITO, C. G., *Anal. Chem.* **34,** 1173 (1962).
300. ESPOSITO, C. G. and SWANN, M. H., *Anal. Chem.* **34,** 1048 (1962).
301. PERCIVAL, D. F., *Anal. Chem.* **35,** 236 (1963).
302. COOK, C. D., ELGOOD, E. J. and SOLOMON, D. H., *Anal. Chem.* **34,** 1177 (1962).
303. MILLER, D. F., SAMSEL, E. P. and COBLER, J. G., *Anal. Chem.* **33,** 677 (1961).
304. BUTTERY, R. G. and STUCKEY, B. N., *J. Agr. Food Chem.* **9,** 283 (1961).
305. JENNINGS, E. C., CURRAN, T. D. and EDWARDS, D. G., 133rd Nat. Meeting Ass. Chem. Soc., San Francisco, April 1958, Abstract p. 48 B, No. 129.
306. JENNINGS, E. C., CURRAN, T. D. and EDWARDS, D. G., *Anal. Chem.* **30,** 1946 (1958).
307. PRIORI, O. and PANETTI, M., *Poliplastic* **8,** 19 (1960).
308. HYDEN, S., *Anal. Chem.* **35,** 133 (1963).
309. PERRY, S. G., *J. Gas Chromatography* **2,** 54 (1964).
310. WIZE, R. W. and SULLIVAN, A. B., *Rubber Age* **91,** 773 (1962).
311. SAWADA, M., YAMAGI, I. and YAMASHINA, T., *J. Soc. Rubber Ind. (Japan)* **35,** 284 (1962).
312. SIRCAR, A. K., GHOSH, A. K. and BANERJEE, D., *J. Indian Chem. Soc.* **38,** 241 (1961).
313. HILTON, C. L., *Rubber Chem. Technol.* **32,** 844 (1959).
314. KABOTA, T., KURIBAYASHI, S. and FURNHAMA, T., *J. Soc. Rubber Ind. (Japan)* **35,** 662 (1962).
315. CORNISH, P. J., *J. Appl. Polymer Sci.* **7,** 727 (1963).
316. FIORENZA, A., BONOMI, G. and SAREDI, A., *Mater. Plast. Elast.* **31,** 1045 (1965).
317. AULER, H., *Gummi Asbest Kunststoffe* **14,** 1024 (1961).
318. KAWAGUCHI, T., UEDA, K. and KOGA, A., *J. Soc. Rubber Ind. (Japan)* **28,** 525 (1955).
319. PARKER, C. A., *J. Royal Inst. Chem.* **81,** 674 (1957).
320. MANN, J., *Trans. Inst. Rubber Ind.* **27,** 232 (1951).
321. STUCKEY, B. N. and OSBORNE, C. E., *J. Am. Oil Chemists Soc.* **42,** 228 (1965).
322. MANN, J., *Trans. Inst. Rubber Ind.* **19,** 72 (1950).
323. HUMMEL, D., *Analysis of Paints, Rubbers and Plastics*, Carl Horser, Munich (1957).
324. McCOY, R. N. and FIEBIG, E. C., *Anal. Chem.* **37,** 593 (1965).
325. DJERASSI, C., and FENESLAU, C., *J. Am. Chem. Soc.* **87,** 5752 (1965).
326. DUFFIELD, A. M., LIGHTNER, D. A., BENGELMANS, R., WILLIAMS, D. H., BUDZIKIEWICZ, H. and DJERASSI, C., *J. Am. Chem. Soc.* **87,** 805 (1965).
327. LEBLANK, R. B., *New Techniques in I.R.-mass Spectrometry* Laboratory, Gulf Coast Spectroscopic Meeting, Beaumont, Texas (1957).
328. DRUSHEL, H. V. and SOMMERS, A. L., *Anal. Chem.* **36,** 836 (1964).
329. PARKER, C. A. and BARNES, W. J., *Analyst* **82,** 606 (1957).
330. PARKER, C. A., *Anal. Chem.* 1961; see Chapter 1, Section 8, table 16.

INDEX

161